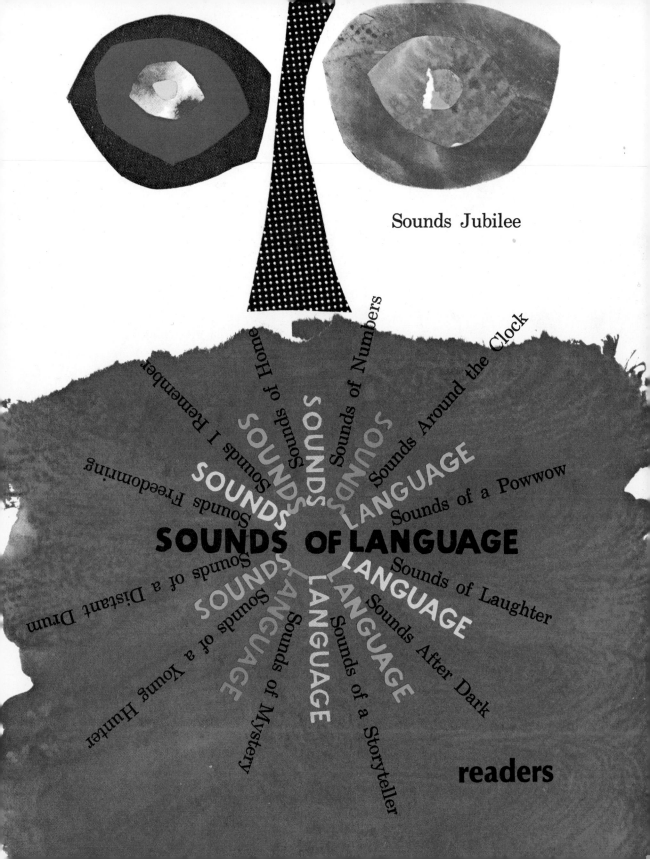

Sounds Jubilee

SOUNDS OF LANGUAGE

Sounds of Numbers
Sounds of Home
Sounds I Remember
Sounds Freedomring
Sounds of a Distant Drum
Sounds of a Young Hunter
Sounds of Mystery
Sounds of a Storyteller
Sounds After Dark
Sounds of Laughter
Sounds of a Powwow
Sounds Around the Clock

readers

Sounds

Jubilee

by Bill Martin Jr.

in collaboration

with Peggy Brogan

Holt, Rinehart and Winston, Inc.
New York, Toronto, London, Sydney

SOUNDS OF LANGUAGE READERS

Acknowledgments

This book is dedicated proudly to
Al Caiola
colleague · guitarist · friend

The Authors and Holt, Rinehart and Winston, Inc., thank the following authors, publishers, agents and parties whose help and permissions to reprint materials have made this book possible. If any errors in acknowledgments have occurred, the errors were inadvertent and will be corrected in subsequent editions as they are realized.

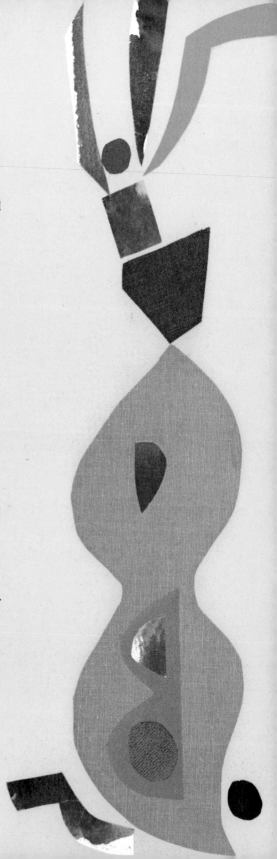

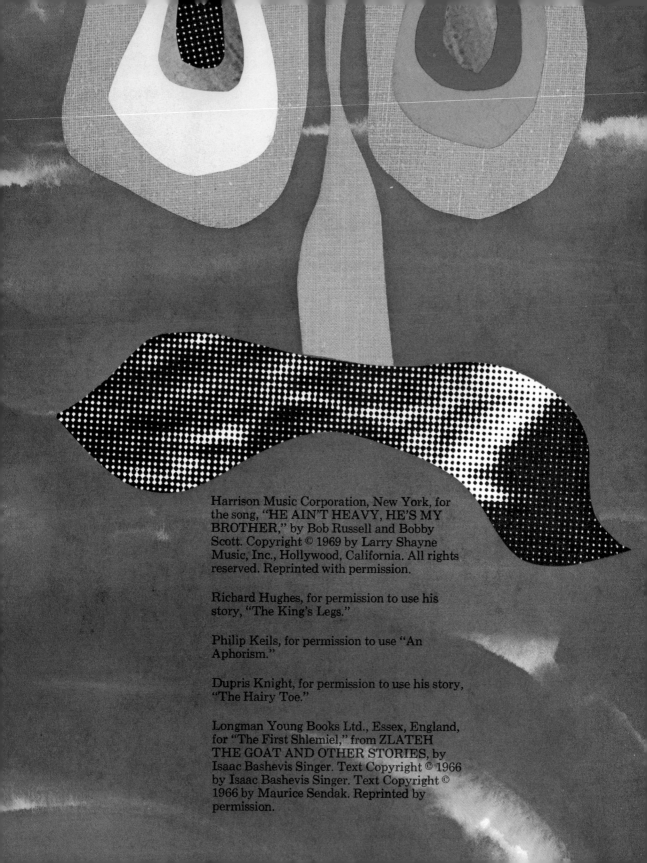

Alexander Resnikoff, for permission to use his story, "The Tale of the Wailing Whale (in a Veil)."

Jesse Rosenberg, for permission to use the poem, "Thoughts."

Prescovia Rwakyaka, for permission to use the story, "House Afire!"

G. Schirmer, Inc., music publishers, for "The Little White Hen," by Antonio Scandello, freely translated by George Howerton. Copyright 1942 by G. Schirmer, Inc. Used with permission.

Ian Serraillier, for permission to use the poem, "The Hen and the Carp."

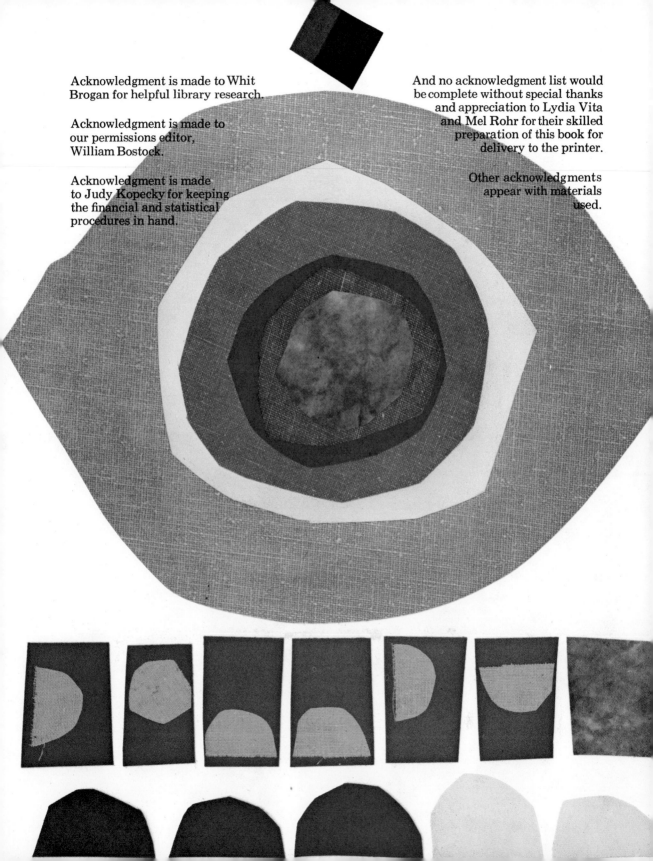

Acknowledgment is made to Whit Brogan for helpful library research.

Acknowledgment is made to our permissions editor, William Bostock.

Acknowledgment is made to Judy Kopecky for keeping the financial and statistical procedures in hand.

And no acknowledgment list would be complete without special thanks and appreciation to Lydia Vita and Mel Rohr for their skilled preparation of this book for delivery to the printer.

Other acknowledgments appear with materials used.

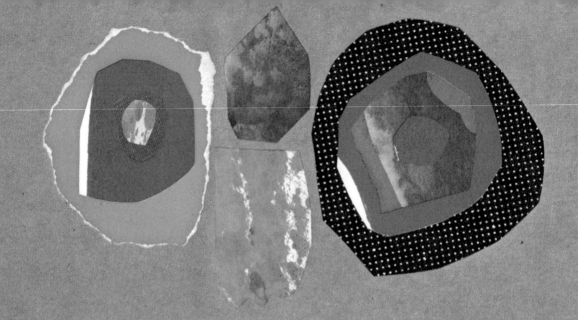

Table of Contents

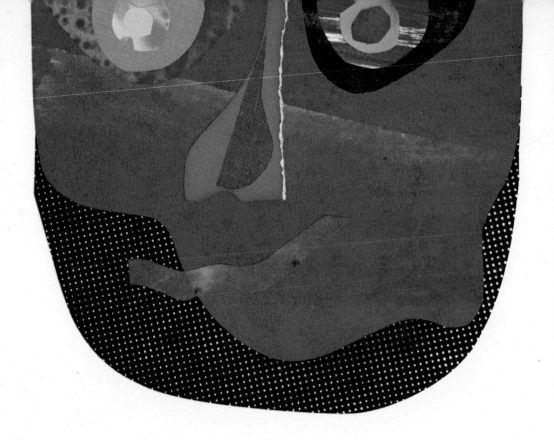

When Johnny Jones was serenading Mary,
He sure could quote a lot of poetry
But he'd much rather tell 'er
what he learned in his speller
when they both attended P.S. Thirty-three.

A you're adorable, B

you're so beautiful, C you're a

cutie full o' charms. D you're a

darling, and E you're exciting,

and F you're a feather in my arms.

"A"-You're Adorable   words and music by Buddy Kaye Fred Wise Sidney Lippman

G you look good to me, **H** you're so heavenly, **I** you're the one I idolize. **J** we're like Jack and Jill, **K** you're so kissable, **L** is the love-light in your eyes.

M N O P I could go on all day.

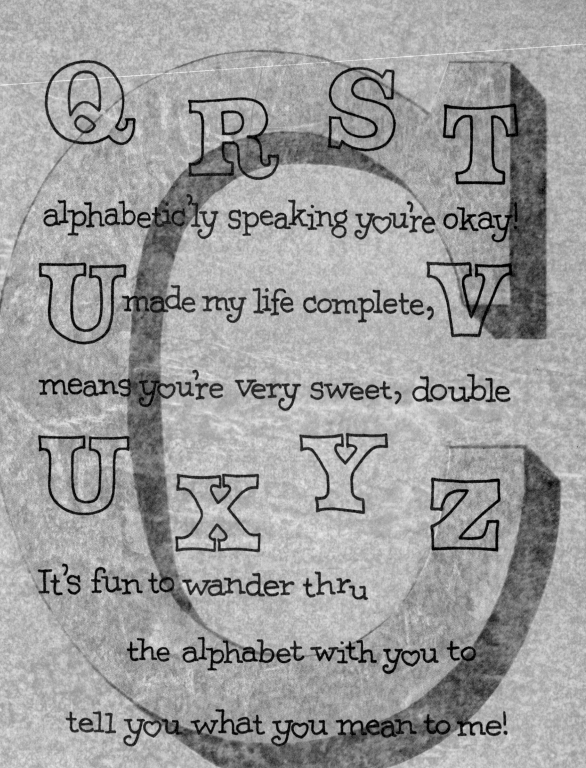

Q R S T
alphabetic'ly speaking you're okay!
U made my life complete, V
means you're very sweet, double
U X Y Z
It's fun to wander thru
the alphabet with you to
tell you what you mean to me!

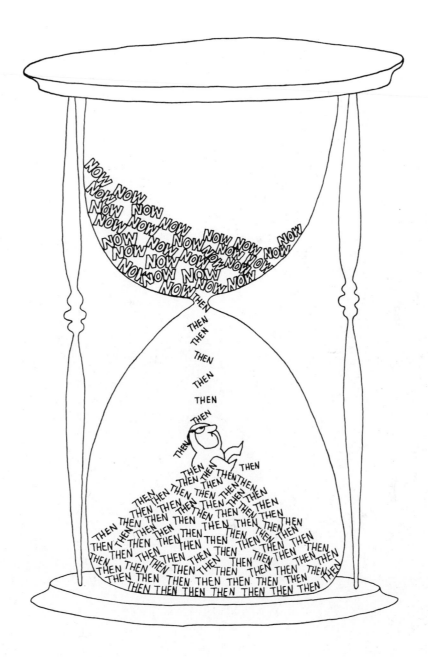

Verse 1

Sometimes I'm right
and I can be wrong,
my own beliefs
are in my song.

The butcher, the banker,
the drummer and then,
makes no diffrence
what group I'm in.

Verse 2

I am no better,
and neither are you.
We are the same
what ever we do.

You love me, you hate me,
you know me and then,
you can't figure out
the bag I'm in.

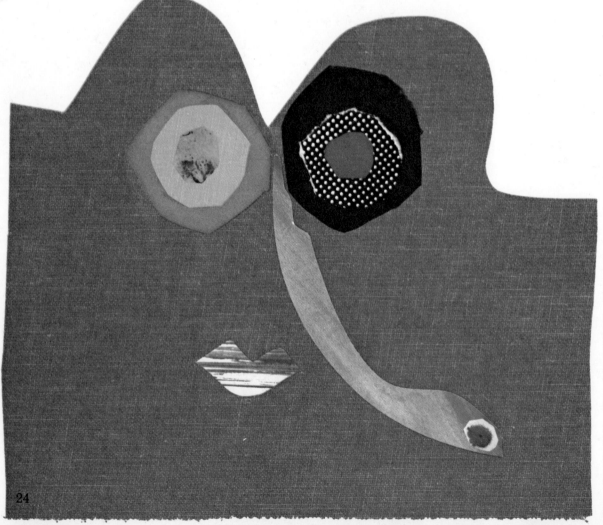

Chorus:

I am Ev'ry day People, yeah, yeah.
There is a blue one who can't accept the green one
    for living with a fat one trying to be a skinny one;
There is a long-hair who doesn't like the short hair
    for being such a rich one that will not help the poor one;
There is a yellow one that won't accept the black one
    that won't accept the red one that won't accept the white one;
And diff'rent strokes for diff'rent folks.
        And so on, and so on,
        and scoo-by doo-by doo-bee . . .
        Doo-sha-sha.
        We got to live together!

I am Ev'ry day People

A SONG BY SYLVESTER STEWART, ART BY SAMUEL MAITIN

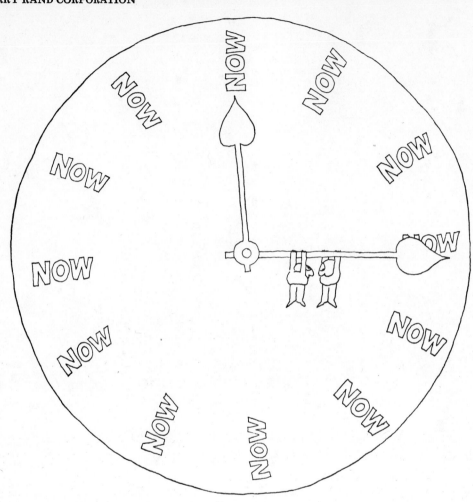

26

A POEM BY WALTER DE LA MARE,
PHOTOGRAPH BY JOEL WELTMAN,
HANDLETTERING BY RAY BARBER.

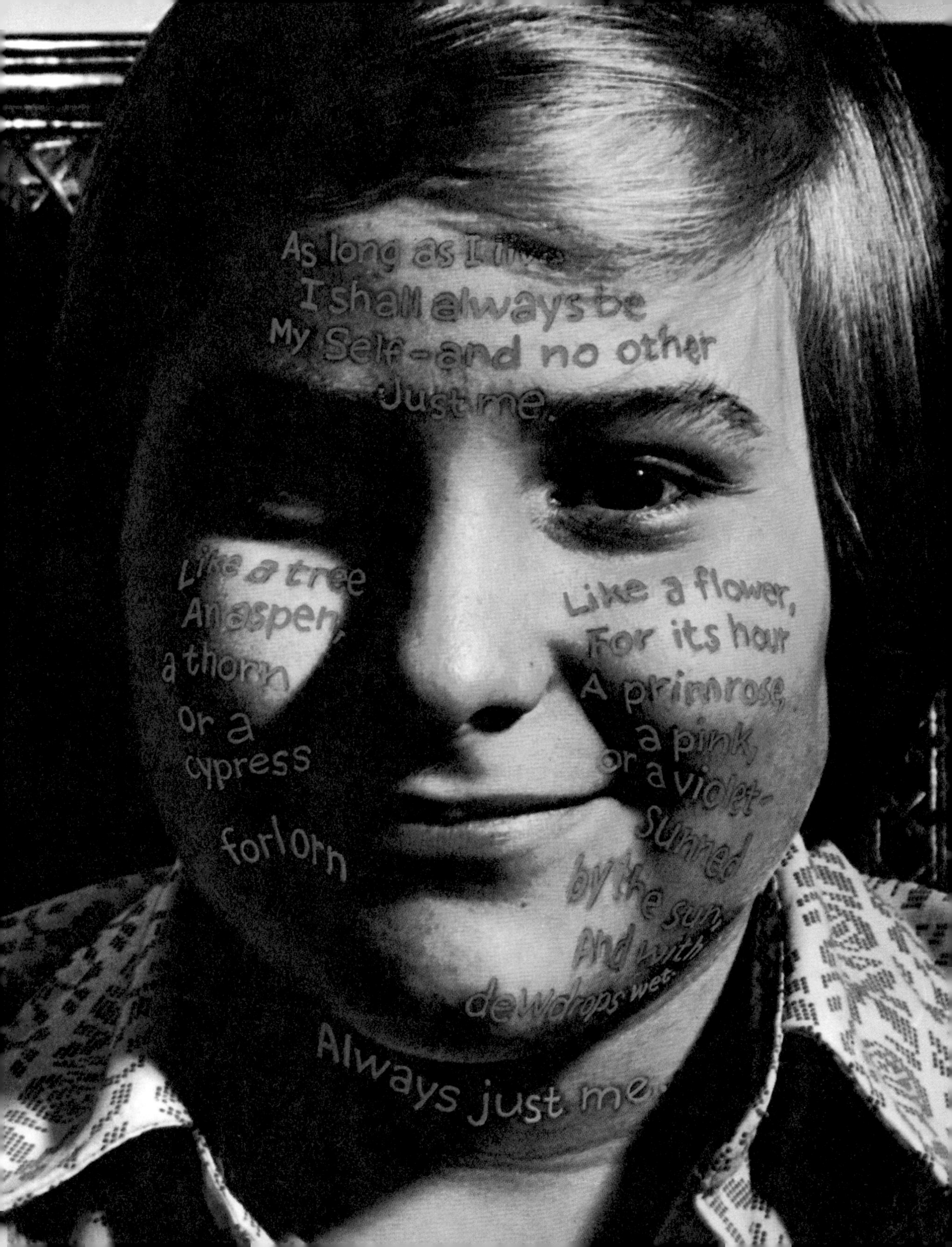

As long as I live
I shall always be
My Self—and no other
Just me.

Like a tree
An aspen,
a thorn
or a
cypress

forlorn

Like a flower,
For its hour
A primrose,
a pink,
or a violet—
sunned
by the sun
And with
dewdrops wet.

Always just me.

Every Man Heart Lay Down

A story by Lorenz Graham,
pictures by Colleen Browning

Long time past
Before you papa live
Before him papa live
Before him pa's papa live—
Long time past
Before them big tree live
Before them big tree's papa live—
That time God live.

And God look on the world
What He done make
And Him heart no lay down.

And He walk about in the town
To see the people
And He sit down in the palaver house
To know the people
And He vex too much.
And God say
   "Nev mind.
    The people no hear My Word
    The people no walk My way
    Nev mind.

    I going break the world and lose the people
    I going make the day dark
    And the night I going make hot.

I going make water that side where land belong
And land that side where water belong.
And I going make a new country
And make a new people."

Now this time
God's one small boy—Him small pican—hear God's word
And the pican grieve for people

So he go fore God's face
And make talk for him Pa.
　　"Pa, I come for Beg You," so he say
　　"I come for beg You,
　　Don't break the world
　　What You done make.
　　Don't lose the people
　　What Yo done care for.
　　I beg you
　　Make it I go
　　I talk to people
　　I walk with people
　　Bye-m-bye they savvy the way."

And the pican go down softly softly
And hold God's foot.
So God look on Him small boy
And Him heart be soft again
And God say

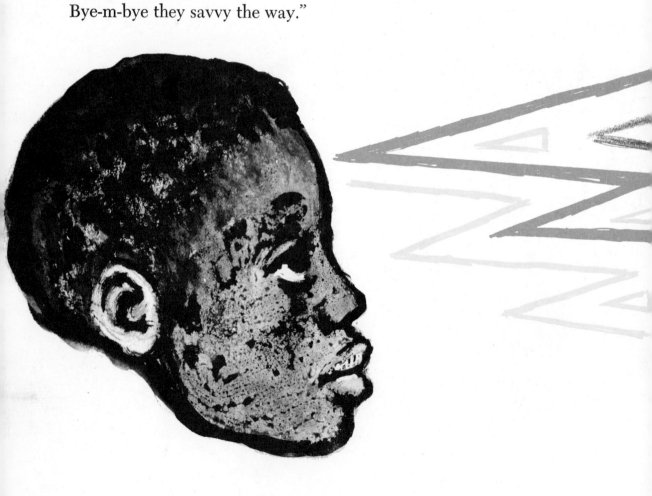

32

"Aye My son,
When you beg me so
I no can vex.
Left me now, but hear me good:
If you go you must be born like a man
And you must live like a man
And you must have hurt and have hunger.

And hear me good:
Men will hate you
And they will flog you
And bye-m-bye they will kill you
And I no going put
My hand there."

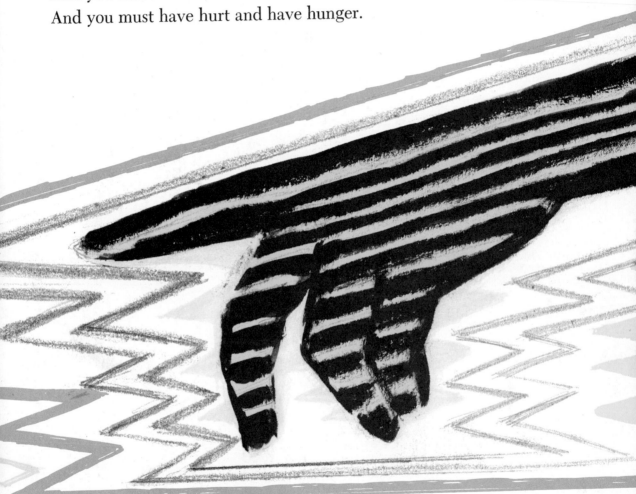

And the pican say
"I agree!"

And bye-m-bye God call Mary
To be ma for the pican.
Now Mary be new wife for Joseph
And Joseph ain't touch Mary self.

So first time Joseph vex.
But God say
    "Nev mind, Joseph,
      This be God palaver."
    And Joseph heart lay down.

And God see one king who try for do good
For all him people
And God say
    "Ahah, Now I send My son
      For be new king."
    And God send star to call the king.

And in a far country
God hear a wise man call Him name
And God say to the wise man
"I send My son to be a new wise man,
Go now with the star."
And the star call
And the wise man follow.

And by the waterside
Men lay down for take rest
And they hear fine music in the sky
Like all the stars make song,
And they fear.

And all the dark make bright like day
And the water shine like fire
And no man can savvy
                And they hearts turn over.
                But God's angel come
                And God's angel say
                "Make glad, all people,
                God's pican be born
                    in Bethlehem."
                    And the people say "Oh."
                    And the wise man
                        And the king

And
    the
  country
people come
  to Bethlehem
    And the star—
come low and stop.

But when they go for mansion house
The star no be there.
And when they go for Big Man's house
The star no be there.
And bye-m-bye when they go for hotel
The star no be there gain—

But the wise man say
    "Ahah, the star be by the small house
        Where cattle sleep!"
And it was so.

And they find Joseph and Mary
And the small small pican
Fold up in country cloth
And the king bring gold for gift
And the wise man bring fine oil
And the country people bring new rice.
And they look on the God pican

AND EVERY MAN HEART LAY DOWN.

39

CHRISTMAS 1969

And lo it came to be that she bore an infant in the subway. Because the apartments cost was too high. She wrapped him in paper towels from a gas station. And lay him on the cold walkway. The train rattled by but no sound came from him.

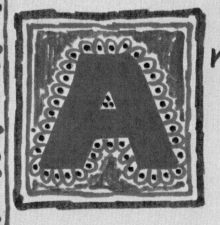

And it came to be that friends heard of him and came to see him. They brought with them gifts of grape drink, cigarettes, and a few dollars.

Kevin Charles

Sixth Grade, Issaquah Valley School,
Issaquah, Washington

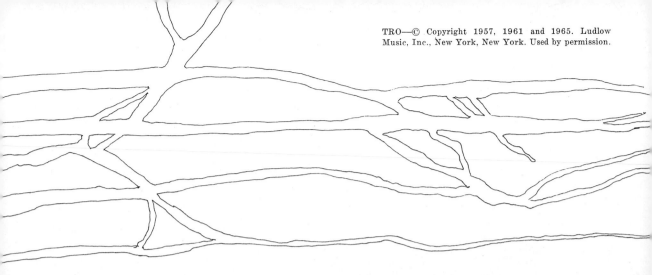

WHEN I FIRST CAME TO THIS LAND

Words and music by Oscar Brand, illustrations by Morgan Harris

When I first came to this land,
I was not a wealthy man.
Then I built myself a shack,
I did what I could.

I called my shack, Break-my-back.
Still the land was sweet and good,
I did what I could.

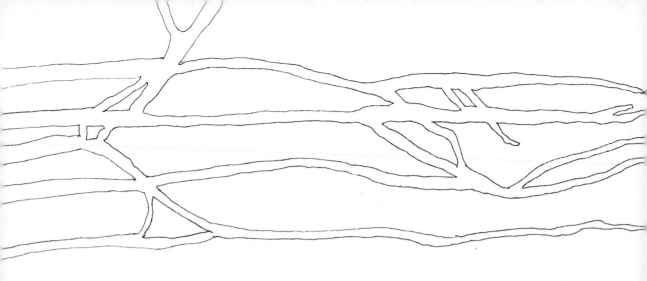

When I first came to this land,
I was not a wealthy man.
Then I bought myself a cow,
I did what I could.

I called my cow, No-milk-now.
I called my shack, Break-my-back.
Still the land was sweet and good,
I did what I could.

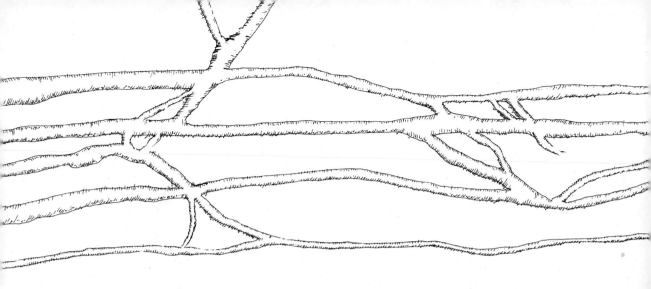

When I first came to this land,
I was not a wealthy man.
Then I bought myself a horse,
I did what I could.

I called my horse, Lame-of-course.
I called my cow, No-milk-now.
I called my shack, Break-my-back.
Still the land was sweet and good,
I did what I could.

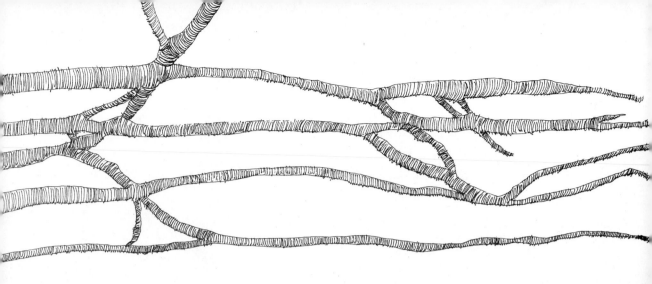

When I first came to this land,
I was not a wealthy man.
Then I bought myself a duck,
I did what I could.

I called my duck, Out-of-luck.
I called my horse, Lame-of-course.
I called my cow, No-milk-now.
I called my shack, Break-my-back.
Still the land was sweet and good,
I did what I could.

When I first came to this land,
I was not a wealthy man.
Then I got myself a wife,
I did what I could.

I called my wife, Joy-of-my-life,
I called my duck, Out-of-luck,
I called my horse, Lame-of-course,
I called my cow, No-milk-now,
I called my shack, Break-my-back.
Still the land was sweet and good,
I did what I could.

When I first came to this land,
I was not a wealthy man.
Then I got myself a son,
I did what I could.

I told my son: "My work's done."
For the land was sweet and good,
I did what I could.

Fleeing to Safety

A POEM BY RAJIV CHETTUR, AGE 10, INDIA

Under the force
Of a Sunday breeze
A Sunday breeze
And the humming waves,
We on a raft of wood
Dancing along
The ocean flood,
To reach,
Far away, our goal,
Away from
The hated souls,
Among God's harmless creatures.
We, on a wooden raft,
A wooden raft
A wooden raft.

From: "MIRACLES" by Richard Lewis

Thoughts

A POEM BY JESSE ROSENBERG,
GRADE 5, P.S. 139, BROOKLYN

I sat in the shade of an oak,
reading,
resting,
thinking,
A bird fluttered down
beside me
saying:

"In every black there is a white,
In every laugh there is a cry
In every heart there is a person
In every day there is a night,
In every hate there is a love!"

Her enchanting voice drew out all the sorrows
of my head,
For her voice was like the singing brook
Her wings were arms stretching towards me,
I reached out
to hold it,
It slipped through my fingers like dirt,
and fluttered away.
"Sister!" I cried, "come back!"
But off she went.
Into the horizon — to die?
Are all birds born —
to die?

PRAIRIE FIRE

A PERSONAL EXPERIENCE STORY BY S. E. BALL,
PAINTING BY ROBERT SHORES

The threat of death by fire
is one of the most terrifying experiences man can know.
To me that experience came
when I was a boy of 9 living on a homestead
in the "Cherokee strip" of Oklahoma.

The claim upon which my father
had built our little prairie home
was covered with blue stem grass
growing in some places
as high as a horse's head.
To the east of our homestead in the Salt Fork valley
lay what was known as "the big pasture."
It was 16 miles long and eight miles wide,
all surrounded by one fence.
Large herds of cattle were pastured there
every summer on the heavy blue stem grass.

At a certain time each spring,
just before the grass began to shoot sprouts
for the new growth,
the cattlemen would burn off the previous year's growth.
They burned fire guards
along the west side of the pasture,
as the settlers had made their new homes to the west,
and also because the spring winds in Oklahoma
blow from the south and west.

After plowing the fire guards
the cattlemen often had to wait some time
for a quiet day and dry weather,
when it would be safe to burn off the pasture.

A quiet day in Oklahoma in the spring
does not occur very often,
as any who have lived there well know.

It was the second spring
we had lived in the valley
when one day our neighbor to the east
came over to tell us that
after sundown that day
the big pasture would be burned off.
We were frightened and excited,
for a pasture fire, even under control,
is a thrilling sight.

As darkness came on
we all went outside to watch the first red glow of light
rise in the sky some 12 miles away.
As we watched,
the glow rose higher and higher,
until the sky looked as though
the whole world were afire.

Because it had not been pastured
during the previous fall,
the grass was thick and tall,
and the fire spread rapidly.
The darkness turned rapidly
to a brilliant glare
as the flames swept across the big pasture.

I have often wondered what my mother thought
as she stood there in the path
of that terrible wall of fire

which was sweeping closer and closer and closer,
higher and brighter every moment.
Did she sense the fact
that the narrow pasture guard would not hold
the terrific fire away from the settlers' homes?

All at once
a huge cloud of smoke came rolling
across our yard.
The wind had changed.
In moments it was blowing very strong,
bringing the fire directly toward us.

My father, like the other settlers,
had plowed guards around the house.
But the little strip was of no value now,
for the fire was plainly out of control.
Father ran to the narrow guard,
and as the roar of the fire came nearer and nearer,
he backfired with every ounce of strength and speed he possessed,
knowing all his feed and shelters for the stock
might be burned. He had succeeded in burning a patch
directly in front of the house,
which he hoped
would keep the head fire from jumping his narrow guard,
when the big fire met the backfire.

My sister and I
stood on the roof of our little house
with buckets of water and wet sacks
to challenge and beat out every flying spark.
The yard grass was short,
and several times fire started there.
But my valiant little mother
was always there to pounce upon it
and beat it out.

The sky was full
of small birds and insects
flying before the fire.
The lower-flying quail and prairie chickens
flew and fluttered on as best they could
in their exhaustion.
Rabbits came, too, and other prairie animals.

The flames came swiftly,
and passed swiftly around our house.
But our hay stacks and livestock shelters were burned.
We learned later that the fire was not headed
until it reached the Salt Fork river
three miles away.

We did not sleep that night,
for we were enveloped
in smoke from the smouldering grass
and buffalo chips.
When morning came
we rode out with Father to see how others had fared.
As we crossed the blackened prairie,
we saw the twisted balls of charred flesh
that had once been a deadly rattlesnake,
seared carcasses of rabbits,
skunks, coyotes and a few deer.
All had lost the race of death.

April showers soon began to fall,
and the new grass came up
and made a green carpet over the valley.
But time and all its changes
can never erase from my memory
that night in the path of a prairie fire.
It was surely
the most vivid experience of my life.

59

Old Hogan's Goat

Was feeling fine.
He ate a red shirt
Right off my line.
I took a stick
And beat his back
And tied him to
A railroad track.
A speeding train
Was adrawin' nigh;
Old Hogan's goat
Was doomed to die.
He gave an aw-
ful shriek of pain
Coughed up that shirt
And flagged that train.

Speak to Me

       darlin',
oh, speaky, spikey, spokey.
Why are those tears
on your cheeky, chikey, chokey?
Give me the answer
I seeky, sikey, sokey!
Or else I'll go jump
in the creeky, crikey, crokey.

ART BY BOB SHEIN

The Happiest Apples

A POEM BY
WILLIAM
PACKARD

always
fall
by

the
weight
of

their
own
patience

Here

A POEM BY
ROBERT
CREELEY

What
has happened
makes

the world.
Live
on the edge,

looking.

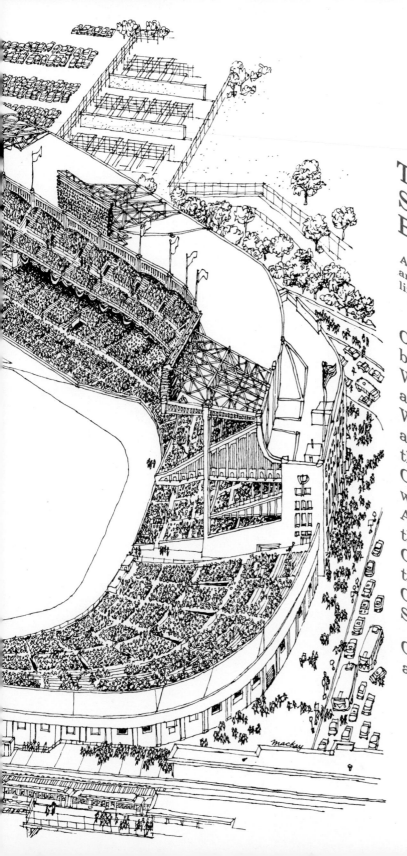

The Star-Spangled Banner

A song with words by Francis Scott Key,
and music by John Stafford Smith,
line drawing by Don Mackay

O say! can you see,
by the dawn's early light,
What so proudly we hail'd
at the twilight's last gleaming?
Whose broad stripes
and bright stars,
thro' the perilous fight,
O'er the ramparts we watch'd,
were so gallantly streaming?
And the rocket's red glare,
the bombs bursting in air,
Gave proof thro' the night
that our flag was still there.
O say, does that
Star-Spangled Banner yet wave

O ★er the land of the free
and the home of the brave?

63

My Parents
Kept Me from Children
Who Were Rough

Who threw words like stones and who wore torn
    clothes.
Their thighs showed through rags. They ran in the
    street
And climbed cliffs and stripped by the country
    streams.

I feared more than tigers their muscles like iron
Their jerking hands and their knees tight on my arms.
I feared the salt-coarse pointing of those boys
Who copied my lisp behind me on the road.

They were lithe, they sprang out behind hedges
Like dogs to bark at my world. They threw mud
While I looked the other way, pretending to smile.
I longed to forgive them, but they never smiled.

A POEM BY STEPHEN SPENDER

Traveling Through the Dark

I found a deer

dead on the edge of the Wilson River road.
It is usually best to roll them into the canyon:
that road is narrow; to swerve might make more dead.

By glow of the tail-light I stumbled back of the car
and stood by the heap, a doe, a recent killing;
she had stiffened already, almost cold.
I dragged her off; she was large in the belly.

My finger touching her side brought me the reason —
her side was warm; her fawn lay there waiting,
alive, still, never to be born.
Beside that mountain road I hesitated.

The car aimed ahead its lowered parking lights;
under the hood purred the steady engine
I stood in the glare of the warm exhaust turning red;
around our group I could hear the wilderness listen.

I thought hard for us all — my only swerving —
then pushed her over the edge into the river.

A POEM BY WILLIAM STAFFORD

65

Once

there was

a man named
Professor Johndear.

He had a wife and two
children. They were
a very agreeable family
except for one great
trouble.

THE MICE
WHO LOVED
WORDS

by Daniel Weiss, illustrations by Dianne Ewell Weiss

The house
the family lived in
had

mice

...the sort of unusual mice
that live in professors' houses.

They did not eat cheese or flour
    or dried peas, or nibble grains of rice
    or the ends of spaghetti.

They were not CARNIVOROUS.

They were not HERBIVOROUS.

They were not GRANIVOROUS.

And they were not OMNIVOROUS.

Carnivores eat
MEAT

Omnivores eat
EVERYTHING

Herbivores eat
VEGETABLES

A Granivore

Professor Johndear said they were VERBIVOROUS,
which means
they ate

WORDS   WORDS

Mrs. Johndear was unusually kindhearted,
and she did not mind the mice because they
never nibbled in her kitchen.
But Professor Johndear
did not love the mice. In fact,
they made him very angry.
He wrote
a great deal —
schoolbooks, spellers
and so forth —

but the verbivorous mice ate up his best words by the dozens.

Exasperating

hee

hee

Exasperating!

The mice did not eat Professor Johndear's shorter words like **and** and **but** and **to** and **from**. They preferred his words which were long and hard— words like **significant** and **behavior** and **obedience** and **digestible**.

Those mice grew very
plump and bold, and they
took to running out and
nibbling words right
off the paper when his
back was turned.

Professor Johndear
was at his wit's end.

He put salt in the ink,
but the mice just loved it.
He tried red hot pepper,
but the mice ate the words anyway,
and kept him up all night
with their sneezing.
He tried keeping his papers
in jars, and under water,
and buried,
but the mice found them every time.

One night Professor Johndear cried out in an unusually loud voice,

"I will teach those mice a lesson! I will set a snap-trap!"

no no no

The children heard him
from their favorite spot behind the sofa.
They were horrified.
"Oh, no!" they cried in unison.
"Please don't set a snap-trap!
That would be too cruel!"

"After all my dear," said Mrs. Johndear,
"they are only mice,
and they don't touch anything around the house
but your larger words.
Perhaps if you used smaller words..."

Professor Johndear was indignant.
"What? Give up my biggest words
for a handful of squeaking rodents?
Surrender to mice? NEVER!"

The children clung to his coat
and begged him most piteously
not to set a snap-trap.
He had to walk about for a whole hour
with them dangling from his coat tails.
It was very uncomfortable
and threatened to tear his coat.
So finally he gave up.

"I will catch them alive in a wire trap," he said. "Then I will let them loose in the woods."

The children agreed to this. So that night Professor Johndear set a trap, all baited with appetizing words.

In the morning, there were the mice in the wire trap, looking very woebegone. They gazed anxiously out at Professor Johndear.

"Aha!" he said. "Now that I've caught you, I shall be able to write in peace."

Professor Johndear carried the mice
about a mile into the thick woods
that lay near his house.
Then he opened the trap and said, **"Scat!"**
The mice ran off into the woods
and Professor Johndear walked home
with the empty trap.

Weeks passed.
Professor Johndear was very happy.
He wrote and wrote—long, complicated words
with absolutely every letter in them.

But the children missed the mice.

Then just around Christmas time,
when the earth was frozen
and the windows were coated with frost,
a peculiar thing happened.

Professor Johndear went down to the mailbox
and discovered that the newspaper
which used to be called the DAILY BUGLE
was now called the AILY UGLE.

And there were
several Christmas cards wishing the Johndear
family a   ERRY   MAS and a
HAP   NEW   EAR.

"DRAT! It's those mice again!"

exclaimed Professor Johndear.

"They've gotten into the mailbox!"

"THE MICE ARE BACK,"

whispered
the children happily
to one another
behind the sofa.

"The poor things,"

sighed Mrs. Johndear,

"nothing but newspapers
and greeting cards to eat,
and here it is
almost
Christmas."

On the last day
before Christmas,
Mrs. Johndear had a great idea.
Without a word to anyone,
she dashed downtown
to do some last minute shopping.

On
Chri
stmas
morning
a large pack
age appeared
among all the
other gifts. "Now
go open the door
for the mice," said
Mrs. Johndear. The
children ran to the door
and called softly, "Here mice,
here mice." Then they went away,
leaving the door open just a crack.

AND THE MICE
CAME BACK

Professor Johndear received,
among other things,
a new typewriter
and a large package of carbon paper.

"Now you can use
the typewriter and your carbon paper
and make extra copies for the mice,"
said Mrs. Johndear to her husband.
"In that way
you and the mice
should both be happy."

And they were.

Going up the hill **whip** me not,

Coming down the hill **hurry** me not,

On level ground **spare** me not,

Loose in the stable **forget** me not,

Of hay and corn **rob** me not,

Of clean water **stint** me not,

With sponge and water **neglect** me not,

Of soft dry bed **deprive** me not,

Tired and hot **wash** me not,

If sick or cold **chill** me not,

With bit or rein oh, **jerk** me not,

And when you are angry **strike** me not.

THE HORSE'S PRAYER

DESIGNED BY ERIC CARLE, PAINTING BY E. GARCIA YATA

Once there was a woman
who went out to pick beans,
and she found a Hairy Toe.
She took the Hairy Toe
home with her,
and that night
when she went to bed,
the wind began to
moan and groan.

Away off in the distance
she seemed to hear a voice
crying,

"The Hairy Toe," a story told by Dupris Knight about 1882, illustrations by Robert J. Lee

*"Who's got my Hair-r-r-ry To-o-o-oe?
Who's got my Hair-r-r-ry To-o-o-oe?"*

The wind rose and began to screech
around the house,
and the woman
covered her head with the quilts.
The voice seemed to come nearer:

"Who's got my Hair-r-r-ry To-o-o-oe?"

The woman scrooched down,
'way down under the covers,
and 'bout that time
the wind 'peared to hit the house,

SWOOOOOOSH,

and the old house creaked and cracked
like somethin' was tryin' to get in.

The voice had come nearer, almost at the door now,
and it said,

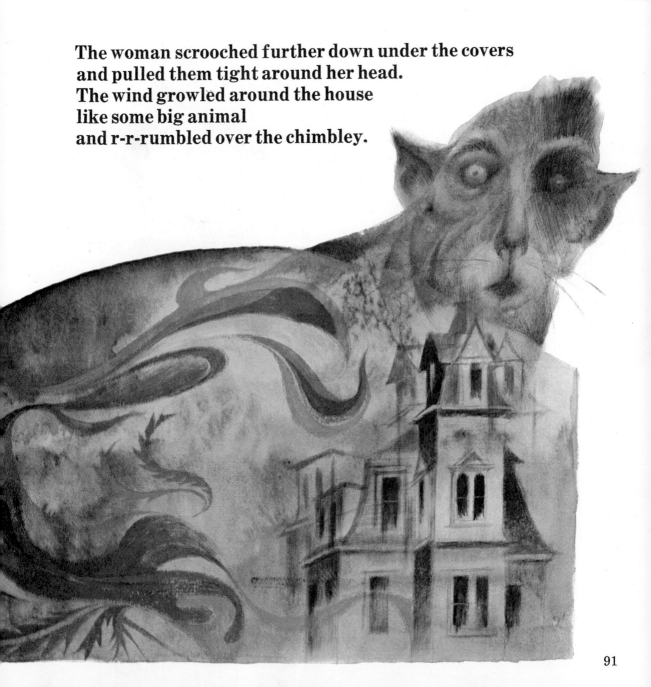

"Where's my Hair-r-r-ry To-o-o-oe?
Who's got my Hair-r-r-ry To-o-o-oe?"

The woman scrooched further down under the covers
and pulled them tight around her head.
The wind growled around the house
like some big animal
and r-r-rumbled over the chimbley.

All at once she heard the door
cr-r-rack open,
and Somethin' slipped in
and began to creep over the floor.
The floor would cre-e-eak,

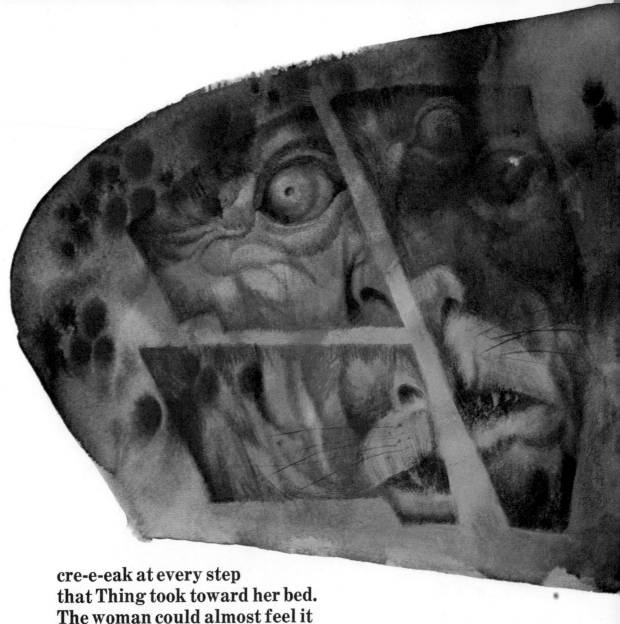

cre-e-eak at every step
that Thing took toward her bed.
The woman could almost feel it
bending over her head over the bed.
Then in an awful voice it said,

"Where's my Hair-r-r-ry To-o-o-oe?
Who's got my Hair-r-r-ry To-o-o-oe?"

"YOU GOT IT!!!"

A STORY BY GREGORY CLARK,
PAINTINGS BY SAMUEL MAITIN

The Whistle

From my window,
I saw a small boy in a cowboy hat.
He was about four years old.
A whistle hung from the cords
of the cowboy hat that go under the chin.

And walking purposefully along the street,
he would give a brief toot on the whistle.
He must have passed and repassed the house
a dozen times, I thought.
I watched him vanish off down the block.

After 5 p.m. I decided
to go for a stroll over to the shopping district
and buy the evening paper.

It was quite a trick to cross the main street
during the rush hour.
I bided my time.
There was no hurry.

And as I stood on the corner,
with other pedestrians, awaiting a break,
I heard in the distance
the small, brief toots on the whistle.

94

Half-way down the block,
up and down which the day's-end traffic was raging,
I saw the little boy in the cowboy hat,
walking slowly southward.
His hat had slipped back on his head.

Well, now, how would a little boy of four get away over here?
Even in two hours?

So I set off after him, and slowed down artfully.

"Hello," I said, as if I were just passing.

The face he turned up was dreadfully tired.
And he had been crying.

"That's quite a whistle you have."

"My daddy will come," replied the child.

"You bet."

"He said if I blew the whistle, he would come."

"He'll be here." I paused and leaned on my stick.
The little fellow ceased walking too.

"What's your daddy's name?"

I saw I had presumed too far. He started to walk on.

"I saw you a little while ago," I mentioned, falling in step.

"You were up near my house.
Do you live near my house?"

No answer.
And the chin sank down on the striped sweater.

"I'm going back to my house.
What street do you live on?"

"My daddy said he would come if I blew my whistle."

"Good. Give it a good blow, now."

The small squeak of the whistle
was like a bird's chirp in the rush of the home-thrusting traffic.

At the end of the block, a policeman stood,
tending a traffic-signal switch.

"Blow," I urged. "Blow."

Together, we proceeded slowly to the corner.

"I think," I said, "we have a young man here
who is in search of his daddy."

The policeman was a young one.

He turned the traffic switch to automatic
and squatted down by the little cowboy.

"My daddy said he would come if I blew my whistle."

"Aha!" nodded the constable.

He stood up and said: "I'll be back in a minute."

He walked over to a post
where the police telephone sits inconspicuously.

"Yes," he said. "They're looking for him.
Been gone since noon."

"Live far away?"

"A good twenty blocks."

"What happens? Does the squad car come for him?"

The young policeman smiled down at me,
very ruddy, very blue in the eye.

"No, sir," said he.

"They'll bring his daddy
and let him out up the block a way.
I arranged that.
Then he can blow his whistle,
and sure enough, his daddy will come."

"Look, son," I said, "you're a pretty
good cop."

"No," he replied,

"I'm the daddy of a kid about just that age."

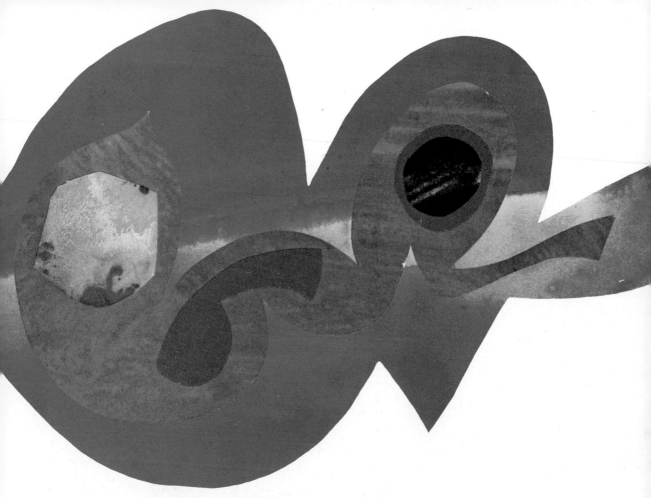

In a few minutes,
  we saw the squad car pull up, half-way up the block.

"Look, cowboy," said the policeman,
  directing the little fellow's attention the wrong way.
"Blow! Blow!"

"Blow!" I added.

  He blew.

And when he turned,
  he saw his daddy running for him with outstretched arms.

The squad car took them away.

The young constable winked at me,
  as he turned the traffic switch back to manual.

A good cop.

you don't have to be

as wise as

Sophocles

to know there's a little

Mephistopheles

in every female

Anopheles

AN APHORISM BY PHILIP KEILS

98

PEOPLE

BY LAURIE GLICK

MACK THE PACK-RAT

A story by Polly Fox,
drawings by Peter Weaver

Mack, the
Pack
Rat,
Sat on a
Spool
Stool,
Smiled at the
Style of his
Domicile.

Match box for a table,
He found in the stable.
For a carpet
He was able
To procure
A brochure.

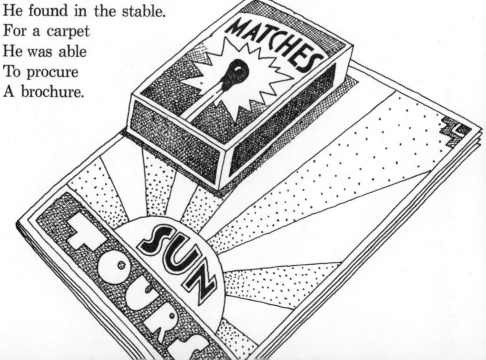

114

For a chair, he used
A hairbow.
He found it at the
Fair so
Mack packed it on his
Back and he
Carried it home.

Did the same
With a bottle cap,
He used it
For a looking glass,
And half
   a U.S. road map's on
The wall in the hall.

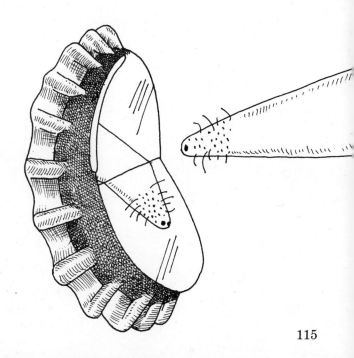

His house was truly gorgeous
Mack decided with a grin.
His treasure was enormous,
His fondest wish had been
Granted, and he'd like to invite you to drop in
To admire all the clutter,
Have some tea and bread and butter,

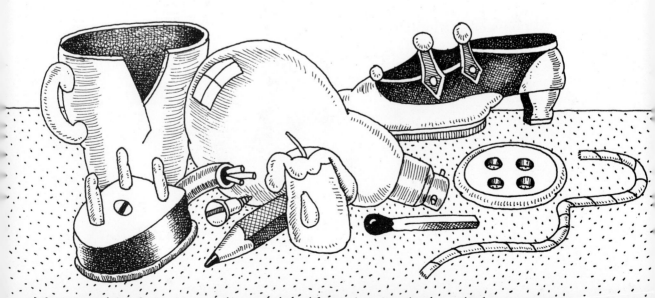

And please to bring a penny or a bright shiny pin!

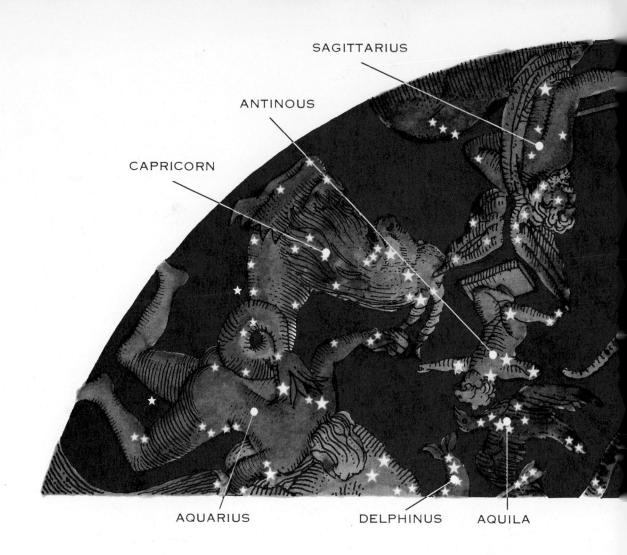

SAGITTARIUS

ANTINOUS

CAPRICORN

AQUARIUS   DELPHINUS   AQUILA

AN ASTROLOGY MAP
IN THREE PARTS
ILLUSTRATIONS BY CHARLES BREY

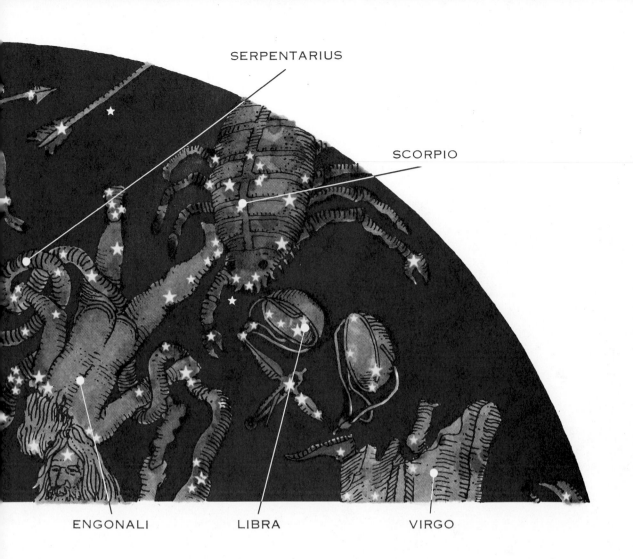

SERPENTARIUS

SCORPIO

ENGONALI   LIBRA   VIRGO

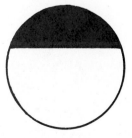

PEGASUS   CYGNUS   DRACO   LYRA

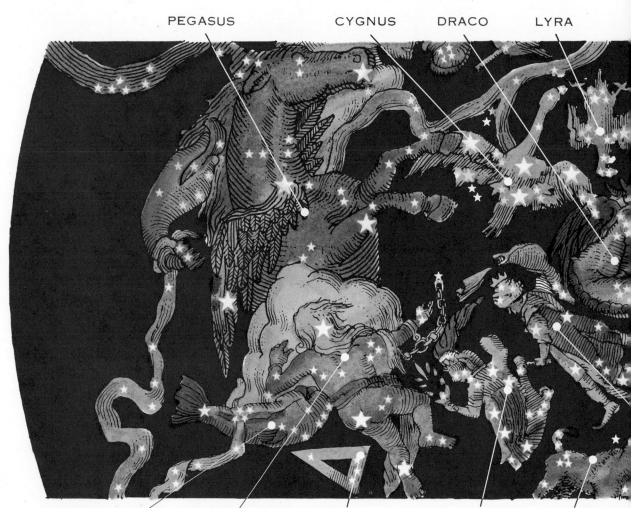

PISCES   ANDROMEDA   TRIANGULUM   CALSIO PEIA   GYRAFFA

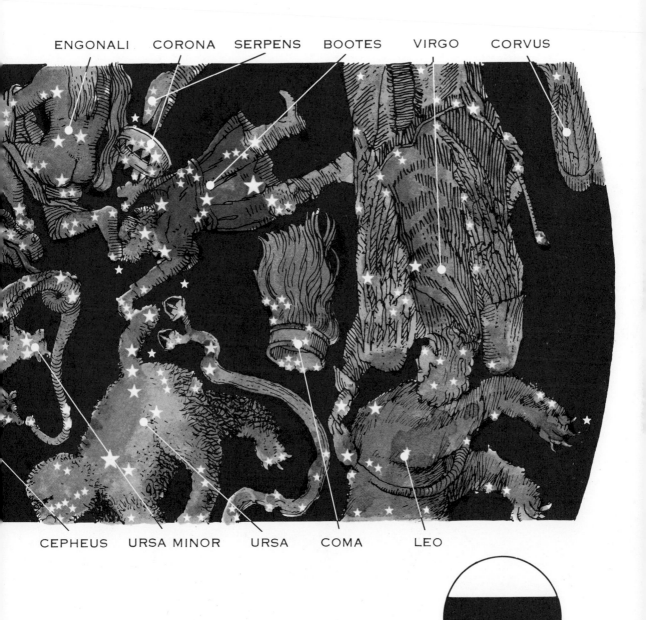

ENGONALI CORONA SERPENS BOOTES VIRGO CORVUS

CEPHEUS URSA MINOR URSA COMA LEO

121

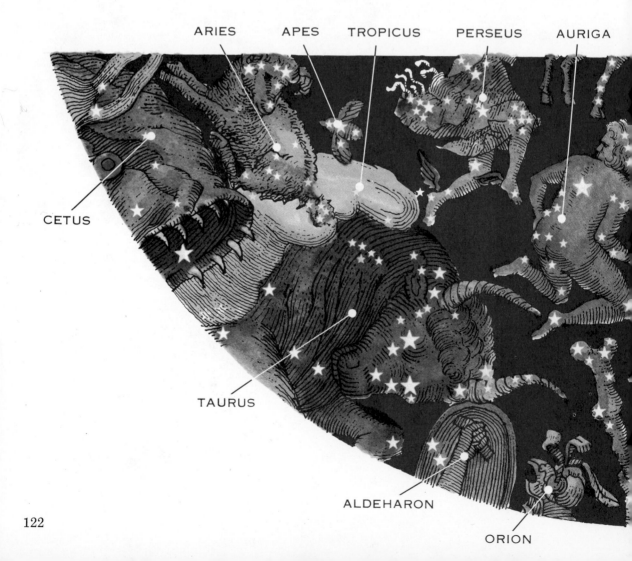

ARIES APES TROPICUS PERSEUS AURIGA

CETUS

TAURUS

ALDEHARON

ORION

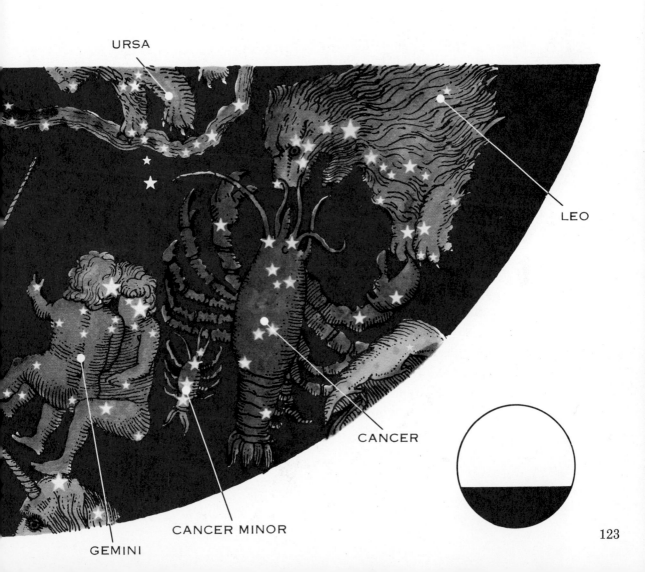

URSA

LEO

CANCER

GEMINI

CANCER MINOR

The First Shlemiel

A STORY BY ISAAC B. SINGER,
PICTURES BY MAURICE SENDAK

here are many shlemiels in the world,
but the very first one came from the village of Chelm.
He had a wife, Mrs. Shlemiel,
and a child, Little Shlemiel,
but he could not provide for them.
His wife used to get up early in the morning
to sell vegetables in the marketplace.
Mr. Shlemiel stayed at home
and rocked the baby to sleep.
He also took care of the rooster
which lived in the room with them,
feeding it corn and water.

Mrs. Shlemiel knew
that her husband was unhandy and lazy.
He also loved to sleep
and had a sweet tooth.
It so happened that one night
she prepared a potful of delicious jam.
The next day she worried
that while she was away at the market,
her husband would eat it all up.
So before she left,
she said to him,

"Shlemiel, I'm going to the market
 and I will be back in the evening.
 There are three things
 that I want to tell you.
 Each one is very important."

"What are they?" asked Shlemiel.

"First, make sure that the baby
 does not fall out of his cradle."

"Good.
 I will take care of the baby."

"Secondly, don't let the rooster
 get out of the house."

"Good.
 The rooster won't get out of the house."

"Thirdly, there is a potful of poison
 on the shelf.
 Be careful not to eat it,
 or you will die,"
 said Mrs. Shlemiel,
 pointing to the pot of jam
 she had placed high up in the cupboard.

She had decided to fool him,
 because she knew
 that once he tasted the delicious jam,
 he would not stop eating
 until the pot was empty.
 It was just before Hanukkah,
 and she needed the jam
 to serve with the holiday pancakes.

s soon as his wife left,
Shlemiel began to rock the baby
and to sing him a lullaby:

> *I am a big Shlemiel,*
> > *You are a little Shlemiel.*
> *When you grow up,*
> > *You will be a big Shlemiel*
> *And I will be an old Shlemiel.*
> > *When you have children,*
> *You will be a papa Shlemiel*
> > *And I will be a grandpa Shlemiel.*

The baby soon fell asleep and Shlemiel dozed too,
still rocking the cradle with his foot.

Shlemiel dreamed
that he had become the richest man in Chelm.
He was so rich
that he could eat pancakes with jam
not only on Hanukkah
but every day of the year.
He spent all day
with the other wealthy men of Chelm
playing games with a golden dreidel.
Shlemiel knew a trick,
and whenever it was his turn to spin the dreidel,
it fell on the winning "G."
He grew so famous
that nobles from distant countries
came to him and said,
"Shlemiel, we want you to be our king."

Shlemiel told them he did not want to be a king.
But the nobles fell on their knees before him
and insisted until he had to agree.
They placed a crown on his head
and led him to a golden throne.
Mrs. Shlemiel, now a queen,
no longer needed to sell vegetables in the market.
She sat next to him, and between them
they shared a huge pancake spread with jam.
He ate from one side and she from the other
until their mouths met.

As Shlemiel sat and dreamed his sweet dream
the rooster suddenly started crowing.
It had a very strong voice.
When it came out with a cock-a-doodle-doo,
it rang like a bell.
Now when a bell rang in Chelm,
it usually meant there was a fire.
Shlemiel awakened from his dream
and jumped up in fright, overturning the cradle.
The baby fell out and hurt his head.
In his confusion Shlemiel ran to the window
and opened it to see where the fire was.
The moment he opened the window,
the excited rooster flew out and hopped away.

Shlemiel called after it,
"Rooster, you come back.
If Mrs. Shlemiel finds you gone,
she will rave and rant
and I will never hear the end of it."

But the rooster paid no attention to Shlemiel.

It didn't even look back,
and soon it had disappeared from sight.

When Shlemiel realized that there was no fire,
he closed the window and went back to the crying baby,
who by this time had a big bump on his forehead
from the fall.
With great effort
Shlemiel comforted the baby,
righted the cradle,
and put him back into it.

Again he began to rock the cradle and sing a song:

> *In my dream I was a rich Shlemiel*
> *But awake I am a poor Shlemiel.*
> *In my dream I ate pancakes with jam;*
> *Awake I chew bread and onion.*
> *In my dream I was Shlemiel the King*
> *But awake I'm just Shlemiel.*

Having finally sung the baby to sleep,
Shlemiel began to worry about his trouble.
He knew that when his wife returned
and found the rooster gone
and the baby with a bump on his head,
she would be beside herself with anger.
Mrs. Shlemiel had a very loud voice,
and when she scolded and screamed,
poor Shlemiel trembled with fear.
Shlemiel could foresee that tonight,
when she got home,
his wife would be angrier than ever before
and would berate him and call him names.

Suddenly Shlemiel said to himself,
"What is the sense of such a life?
I'd rather be dead."
And he decided to end his life.
But how to do it?
He then remembered
what his wife had told him in the morning
about the pot of poison that stood on the shelf.

"That's what I will do.
I will poison myself.
When I'm dead
she can revile me as much as she likes.
A dead Shlemiel does not hear
when he is screamed at."

Shlemiel was a short man
and he could not reach the shelf.
He got a stool,
climbed up on it,
took down the pot,
and began to eat.

"Oh, the poison tastes sweet,"
he said to himself.
He had heard
that some poisons have a bitter taste
and others are sweet.
"But," he reasoned,
"sweet poison is better than bitter,"
and proceeded to finish up the jam.
It tasted so good,
he licked the pot clean.

After Shlemiel had finished the pot of poison,
he lay down on the bed.
He was sure that the poison
would soon begin to burn his insides
and that he would die.
But half an hour passed
and then an hour,
and Shlemiel lay
without a single pain in his belly.

"This poison works very slowly,"
Shlemiel decided.
He was thirsty
and wanted a drink of water,
but there was no water in the house.
In Chelm
water had to be fetched
from an outside well,
and Shlemiel was too lazy
to go and get it.

Shlemiel remembered
that his wife was saving a bottle of apple cider
for the holidays.
Apple cider was expensive
but when a man is about to die,
what is the point of saving money?
Shlemiel got out the bottle of cider
and drank it down to the last drop.

Now Shlemiel began to have an ache
in his stomach,
and he was sure
that the poison had begun to work.

Convinced that he was about to die,
he said to himself,
"It's not really so bad to die.
With such poison
I wouldn't mind dying every day."
And he dozed off.

e dreamed again that he was a king.
He wore three crowns on his head,
one on top of the other.
Before him stood three golden pots:
one filled with pancakes,
one with jam,
and one with apple cider.
Whenever he soiled his beard with eating,
a servant wiped it for him with a napkin.

Mrs. Shlemiel, the queen,
sat next to him on her separate throne
and said,
"Of all the kings who ever ruled in Chelm,
you are the greatest.
The whole of Chelm pays homage
to your wisdom.
Fortunate is the queen of such a king.
Happy is the prince who has you as a father."

hlemiel was awakened
by the sound of the door creaking open.
The room was dark
and he heard his wife's screechy voice.
"Shlemiel, why didn't you light the lamp?"

"It sounds like my wife, Mrs. Shlemiel,"
Shlemiel said to himself.
"But how is it possible that I hear her voice?
I happen to be dead.
Or can it be
that the poison hasn't worked yet
and I am still alive?"
He got up,
his legs shaking,
and saw his wife lighting the lamp.

Suddenly she began to scream
at the top of her lungs.
"Just look at the baby!
He has a bump on his head.
Shlemiel, where is the rooster,
and who drank the apple cider?
Woe is me!
He drank up the cider!
He lost the rooster
and let the baby get a bump on his head.
Shlemiel, what have you done?"

"Don't scream, dear wife,
I'm about to die.
You will soon be a widow."

"Die? Widow?
What are you talking about?
You look healthy as a horse."

"I've poisoned myself,"
Shlemiel replied."

"Poisoned? What do you mean?"
asked Mrs. Shlemiel.

"I've eaten your potful of poison."

And Shlemiel pointed
to the empty pot of jam.

"Poison?" said Mrs. Shlemiel.
"That's my pot of jam for Hanukkah."

"But you told me it was poison,"
Shlemiel insisted.

"You fool," she said.
"I did that to keep you from eating it
before the holiday.
Now you've swallowed the whole potful."
And Mrs. Shlemiel burst out crying.

Shlemiel too began to cry,
but not from sorrow.
He wept tears of joy
that he would remain alive.
The wailing of the parents woke the baby
and he too began to yowl.

W hen the neighbors heard all the crying,
they came running
and soon all of Chelm knew the story.
The good neighbors took pity on the Shlemiels
and brought them a fresh pot of jam
and another bottle of apple cider.
The rooster,
which had gotten cold and hungry
from wandering around outside,
returned by itself
and the Shlemiels had a happy holiday after all.

As always in Chelm
when an unusual event occurred,
the Elders came together to ponder over
what had happened.
For seven days and seven nights
they sat wrinkling their foreheads
and tugging at their beards,
searching for the true meaning of the incident.
At the end
the sages all came to the same conclusion:
A wife who has a child in the cradle
and a rooster to take care of
should never lie to her husband
and tell him that a pot of jam
is a pot of poison,
or that a pot of poison
is a pot of jam,
even if he is lazy,
has a sweet tooth,
and is a shlemiel besides.

Test Your Hockey I. Q.

BY JEFF DOCKING, AGE 11 YEARS, ART BY TED RAND

1. Who was the first goalie
   to wear a mask?
2. Who has scored the most goals
   in hockey's history?
3. Who holds the record of most assists
   in one season by a defenseman?
4. Which goalie in the National Hockey
   League is also a lawyer?

5. Who is the only player in
   National Hockey League history
   to die as a result
   of an on-the-ice accident?
6. In his rookie year, he set
   the record for shutouts
   in one season, for the modern era.
   Who is he?

Answers on page 183.

7. Who scored the winning goal
   to end the 1969 Stanley Cup final?
8. What hockey player is nicknamed
   "The golden jet?"
9. Who was the rookie of the year
   in 1970-71?
10. What player clocked the most
    penalty time in one season?

11. Who received the Most Valuable
    Player award for Stanley Cup
    play in 1968-69?
12. Who holds the record
    for most consecutive
    games played?
13. What is the official size
    of a hockey "rink?"

THE LITTLE WHITE HEN

BY ANTONIO SCANDELLO (1517-1580), TRANSLATED BY GEORGE HOWERTON

This is a choral reading. The color coding cues each group when to read. Many times the four are reading simultaneously, each saying the same thing. It's pure fun!

All: A little white hen, a little white hen with fluffy feathers

looks for food, for golden grain. A little white hen,

a little white hen with fluffy feathers looks for food,

for golden grain.

GROUP 1:	Ka ka ka ka. ka ka nay, ka ka nay,
GROUP 2:	O hear her cackle call! Ka ka ka ka ka ka nay, ka ka ka ka ka
GROUP 3:	Ka ka ka ka ka ka nay, ka ka nay,
GROUP 4:	ka ka ka ka ka ka nay, ka ka nay,

GROUP 1:	ka ka ka ka nay, ka ka nay, the hen lays us an egg,
GROUP 2:	ka nay - - - ka ka nay, ka ka nay, the hen lays us an egg,
GROUP 3:	ka ka nay, ka ka nay - - the hen lays us an egg,
GROUP 4:	ka ka ka ka nay, ka ka nay the hen lays us an egg,

GROUP 1:	ka ka ka ka nay,
GROUP 2:	ka ka ka ka nay,
GROUP 3:	ka ka ka ka nay,
GROUP 4:	ka ka ka ka nay,

ka ka ka ka nay, ka ka nay, ka ka ka ka nay,

ka ka nay – ka ka nay – ka ka nay – ka ka ka ka nay,

ka ka nay – ka ka nay – ka ka nay – ka ka ka ka nay,

ka ka nay – ka ka nay – ka ka nay – ka ka ka ka nay,

GROUP 1:   the hen lays us an egg.
GROUP 2:   the hen lays us an egg.
GROUP 3:   the hen lays us an egg.
GROUP 4:   the hen lays us an egg.

All: Baker make us little pies and little cakes,

spicey cakes with frosting sweet. We'll eat the cakes and drink

the wine. We'll eat the cakes and drink the wine,

and drink the wine.

GROUP 1:   Ka ka ka ka ka ka nay, ka ka nay,
GROUP 2:   Ka ka ka ka ka ka nay, ka ka ka ka nay, ka ka ka ka ka ka
GROUP 3:   Ka ka ka ka ka ka nay, ka ka nay,
GROUP 4:   Ka ka ka ka ka ka nay, ka ka nay,

GROUP 1:   ka ka ka ka nay,   ka ka nay,   the hen lays us an egg,
GROUP 2:   nay,   ka ka nay, ka ka nay,   the hen lays us an egg,
GROUP 3:   ka ka nay, ka ka nay,   the hen lays us an egg,
GROUP 4:   ka ka ka ka nay, ka ka nay,   the hen lays us an egg,

GROUP 1:   ka ka ka ka nay,
GROUP 2:   ka ka ka ka nay,
GROUP 3:   ka ka ka ka nay,
GROUP 4:   ka ka ka ka nay,

ka ka ka ka nay, ka ka nay, ka ka ka ka nay,
ka ka nay, ka ka nay, ka ka nay, ka ka ka ka nay,
ka ka nay, ka ka nay, ka ka nay, ka ka ka ka nay,
ka ka nay, ka ka nay, ka ka nay, ka ka ka ka nay,

All: the hen lays us an egg, the hen lays us an egg.

HOUSE AFIRE!

A PERSONAL EXPERIENCE REMEMBERED BY PRESCOVIA RWAKYAKA,
WATERCOLORS BY WILLI BAUM

I remember one afternoon in particular,
when I was a child.
We had our kitchen heaped as usual
with dry banana leaves for burning.

In our part of the country, Western Uganda,
it rains a great deal.
We often use dry brown leaves
of the banana plant for firewood,
especially during wet weather.
The banana leaves dry out much faster than wet wood.
Also, you can collect the banana leaves in a hurry,
whereas with firewood,
you have to go so far into the bush to find it
that the rain often comes while you're still searching.

My mother was away at the time
(I think she was in the hospital)
and I was left in charge of the kitchen.
I was cooking beans, I think it was.
My younger brother was outside playing.
The boys of the neighborhood had gathered to play football,
using a ball made of banana fibre.
I was attracted by the play,
and would stop from time to time while I worked
to watch the game.
In fact, I kept edging closer and closer to the door
till I finally moved outside,
watching and cheering and really becoming absorbed.

After a while,
realizing that I should be giving some attention to my cooking,
I turned back.
Smoke was coming out of the kitchen door, then fire!
To my horror, the cooking fire had spread,
catching on to the dry banana leaves
and going up and up.

A flame leapt up to catch one corner of the thatched roof!
"Quick! Quick!" I screamed to the boys.
"The kitchen is burning!
The roof is on fire!"
My brother and his friends came running,
to see fire and smoke filling the place.
Fortunately there was a large drum of water
just outside the big house.
All of us grabbed up
whatever containers we could find,
and began rushing back and forth,
dipping the containers into the drum
and running to the kitchen to pour the water on the fire.
We threw water up on the roof, too, all of us
fighting the fire wherever it broke out.

"This is only making the fire more furious!"
one boy screamed. "Let's use soil!"

We started scooping up the soil,
which by now was all wet,
and throwing it on the fire.
To our great relief,
the wet soil smothered the fire.
All the children of the neighborhood had gathered around.
There was nothing left to see but smoke
—and a big hole in the roof!

Now I became truly frightened.
What would I tell my parents?
They would punish me, I was sure,
for I knew very well that in our tribe,
when a girl was given responsibility for cooking
or any such work in the home,
she was not expected to leave her task
and go outside at any time
—especially if it was boys she was watching.
My brother knew this, too.
He offered to gather reeds,
to cut them, and to plait the roof.
He said he would try
to tie the reeds over the hole
so the patch wouldn't show.
The neighbor boys helped him gather the reeds;
then they left him to mend the roof by himself.
He was as frightened as I was,
so he worked very hard.

In the meantime, I went to the bush to collect more fuel;
the nice heap of dry banana leaves for cooking had burned completely.
Fearful as I was,
I welcomed the chance to leave the house,
leaving my brother to face our father.
But it was just as I was coming back with my load of leaves
that I heard my father returning from work.
My brother was still on the roof, tying the reeds together.

"What on earth are you doing?"
I heard my father ask the boy.
"I'm mending the roof," my brother called down.

"What happened?"
"The kitchen was burning...and the roof caught on fire.
"But how did it start?"
"Well...the leaves caught fire in the kitchen."

Certain that I knew what was coming,
I watched and listened in fear
but to my surprise, my father became very sympathetic.
He could understand, he said,
how easily the dry leaves would burn.
He was only glad that his children were not harmed.
(In fact, it was after this incident that he started to buy firewood.)
The two of us felt lucky.
When we saw that our father
was not going to scold or to punish us at all,
my brother went right on plaiting the roof
and I went right on with the cooking.

Take some paper from a drawer,
Just one piece, not any more,
To make a fish.

Put the paper on a dish.
Make a wish.
Cut out the fish.

Color in its yellow gills
Cover it with polka pills
Cook the fish.

Serve it on a serving dish.
It's delish.
Eat the fish.

POEM "HOW TO MAKE A FISH" BY JOHN BECKER,
PAINTING "JAZZ" BY MERLE SHORE

The Tale of the Wailing Whale

A STORY BY ALEXANDER RESNIKOFF,
ART BY PETER LIPPMAN

There is a tale of Mr. Snail,
a famous detective from north of Yale,
who one day in his daily mail
received this letter:

"Hail, dear Snail,
a whale has escaped from my jail.
Since you say you never fail
once you're on a culprit's trail,
bring that whale back to jail
and I'll be yours, truly."

It was signed Mr. Quail.
The jailer of the jail in Yale.

Mr. Snail in next day's mail
dispatched a letter to the jail
in which he wrote: "Dear, Quail,
I will not fail to catch that whale
but, one detail.
Is this whale male or female?"

150

"Dear Snail,"
wrote Mr. Quail in next day's mail,
"that whale is a female, not male.
Bring her back to jail!
I'll pay you a whale of a fee!"

"Dear Quail," wrote Mr. Snail,
"I promise I'll nail that female,
but let me know before I sail,
was she dark or was she pale?"

"That female whale was very pale"
wrote Mr. Quail by daily mail.
"Please do not delay, find her trail
and bring that pale whale back to jail!"

"Dear Quail of jail in Yale,"
next morning wrote Detective Snail,
"still concerning that female whale,
any other detail to help me trail her down?"

"That female whale" wrote Mr. Quail,
"always wore a heavy veil.
Please do not delay, do not fail.
Find that pale veiled female whale
and bring her back to the Yale jail!"

"About that whale," wrote Mr. Snail
And mailed it in the daily mail,
"Why, so pale? Why the veil?
Wasn't she happy?"

"Oh, Snail," wrote Mr. Quail,
"that female whale was very frail,
 wouldn't drink water, only ale.
 She always drank it by the pail.
 Then whale would pale and finally ail,
 claiming that the ale was stale.
 Our jail she then would assail,
 demanding a fairy-tale at bedtime.
 Oh, how she'd cry! how she'd wail!
 catching her teardrops in a pail.
 Every time she would exhale,
 she shook the prison with a gale,
 thrashing and smashing her saucy tail
 to prove she was an ailing whale."

"Dear Quail," wrote Mr. Snail,
"stop worrying about that whale
 for tonight I'll sail,
 no matter what it might entail —
 neither rain nor storm nor sleet nor hail
 will swerve me from the trail
 until I bring her back to jail —
 that ailing wailing female whale!"

Before he sailed, Detective Snail
received a cable from the jail:
"Hail, dear Snail,
 the more I think about that whale,
 the way she'd ail, the way she'd wail
 the way she drank up all our ale,
 the way she'd thrash her saucy tail,
 the less I want her back in jail.
 Thanks for your trouble."

"Dear Quail," wrote Mr. Snail
"you cannot prevail upon me
  to quit when I am on a trail
  of a notorious jail-breaking whale.
I've been never known to fail.
I'll bring that whale back to jail —
unless . . .
unless, dear Quail . . .
you . . . ahem . . . would like to pay me double scale . . .
to . . . how shall I say it? . . . not to tail that whale."

"Hey, Snail," wired Mr. Quail
"This is blackmail!
  I would much rather pay the bail
  To keep that female out of jail!"

"Hey, Quail," wrote Mr. Snail,
"you call me a blackmailer by mail?!
Be careful or you'll end in jail
together with your silly whale!"

"*A silly whale?!!*" wrote Mr. Quail.
"A silly whale!" wrote Mr. Snail.

"*And me in jail?!*" wrote Mr. Quail.
"Yes, you in jail!" wrote Mr. Snail.

"Watch what you say!" wrote Mr. Quail,
"or I'll jail you like that whale!"

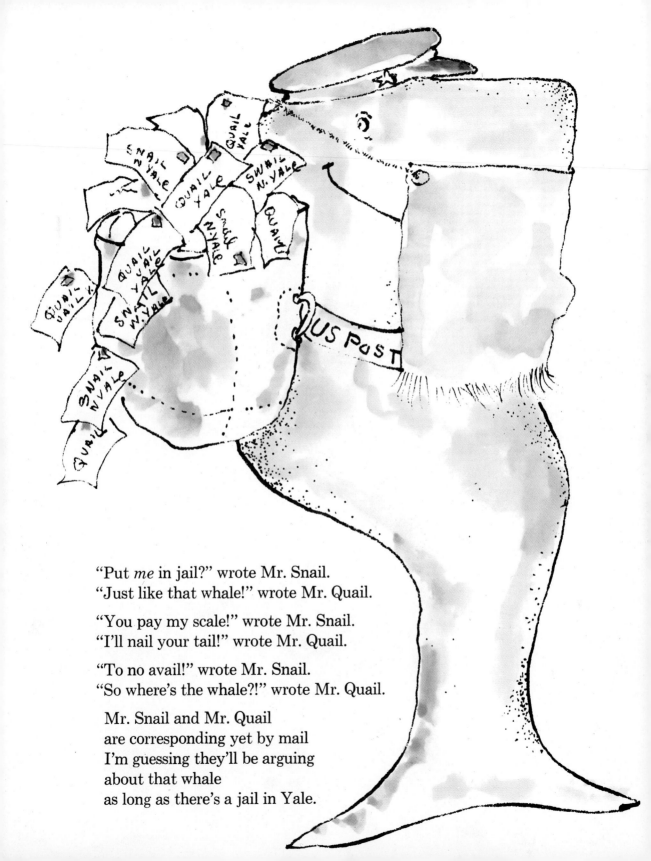

"Put *me* in jail?" wrote Mr. Snail.
"Just like that whale!" wrote Mr. Quail.

"You pay my scale!" wrote Mr. Snail.
"I'll nail your tail!" wrote Mr. Quail.

"To no avail!" wrote Mr. Snail.
"So where's the whale?!" wrote Mr. Quail.

Mr. Snail and Mr. Quail
are corresponding yet by mail
I'm guessing they'll be arguing
about that whale
as long as there's a jail in Yale.

A POEM BY ROSEMARY AND STEPHEN VINCENT BENÉT,
ILLUSTRATION COURTESY OF JACK BRYNE ADVERTISING
FOR BARNEY'S CLOTHES, NEW YORK.

ABRAHAM LINCOLN

1809-1865

Lincoln was a long man.
He liked out of doors.
He liked the wind blowing
And the talk in country stores.

He liked telling stories,
He liked telling jokes.
"Abe's quite a character,"
Said quite a lot of folks.

Lots of folks in Springfield
Saw him every day,
Walking down the street
In his gaunt, long way.

Shawl around his shoulders,
Letters in his hat.
"That's Abe Lincoln."
They thought no more than that.

Knew that he was honest,
Guessed that he was odd,
Knew he had a cross wife
Though she was a Todd.

Knew he had three little boys
Who liked to shout and play,
Knew he had a lot of debts
It took him years to pay.

Knew his clothes and knew his house.
"That's his office, here.
Blame good lawyer, on the whole,
Though he's sort of queer.

"Sure, he went to Congress, once.
But he didn't stay.
Can't expect us all to be
Smart as Henry Clay.

"Need a man for troubled times?
Well, I guess we do.
Wonder who we'll ever find?
Yes—I wonder who."

That is how they met and talked.
Knowing and unknowing.
Lincoln was the green pine.
Lincoln kept on growing.

DRAWING BY CHARLES CHILD

THE GREAT GENIUS

BY TED BERRIGAN

The Great Genius is
A man who can do the
Average thing when everybody
Else is going crazy.

Sampson Solomon was the biggest boaster in town.
Believe me, that cat had a most excellent opinion of himself.
Boasting just came natural to Sampson.
Now I'm sure nobody would have minded his boasting
one speck of snuff if it wasn't for the fact
that he could live up to every boast he made.
When Sampson said,
"My Pop is bigger than your Pop,"
he just wasn't kidding.
Mr. Hercules Solomon was at least eight feet tall.
And I say *at least*,
because there was no one in town tall enough,
or maybe I should say brave enough,
to measure him.
So no one knew for sure that Mr. Solomon wasn't
just as tall as Sampson said he was.

THE SPINNING TOP

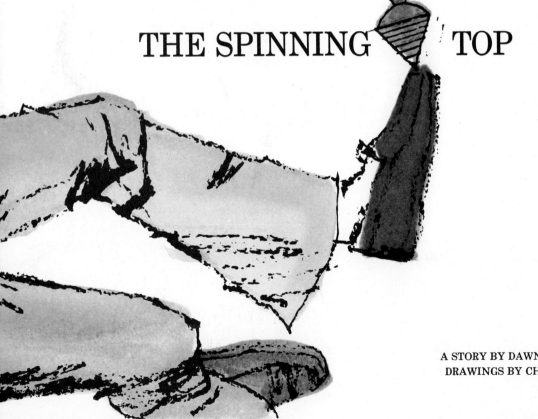

A STORY BY DAWN C. THOMAS,
DRAWINGS BY CHARLES BREY

And when Sampson said his mother was the best baker in the country,
he wasn't putting on.
Sapphire Solomon held the national title of,
Mrs. Cookie-Cake-and-Rolls.
She had been on television to bake a cake,
so nobody would be dumb enough to say
that Sapphire Solomon wasn't the best baker around.
Yes, Sampson was a bragger,
but Sampson was generous.
Every afternoon, he had kids over to sample his mother's cookies
or some other sweet-tooth stuff.

Well, one afternoon all the kids were sitting on Sampson's stoop
when along comes Roscoe.
Next to Sampson, Roscoe is the biggest boaster in town.
We could see that Roscoe had some kind of a thing in his hand.
It was a top.
Weird-looking, but it was a top.
Sampson saw it, but he didn't say nothing.
He just sat there ramming blueberry pie down his throat.

"How you doing, Champ?" Roscoe said to Sampson.

Believe me, that was a war cry if I had ever heard one.
For no one called Sampson just *plain old ordinary* champ.
He liked to be called *Champ of Everything*,
Failure at Nothing.
Sampson always wanted full credit for his talents.

Sampson didn't even look up.
He finished the pie and wiped his mouth
on the left sleeve of his shirt.

"Sampson!" snapped Roscoe,
"didn't you hear me talking to you?"

Sampson raised his head slowly.
A blueberry was locked in the dimple at the top of his lip.
"Was that you talking, Roscoe?
I thought it was Mr. Perez snoring again."

Score round one for Sampson.
Roscoe did have a bad speaking voice.
Somebody behind me let out a little laugh.

Well, if you've ever seen biscuits rise in the oven,
you have some idea of how Roscoe started to swell up—with anger.
He pulled his cap down over one eye
and came up on the first step of the stoop.

"Don't crowd me, Sampson," he warned.

"Boy, why don't you sit down and help yourself to some sweets."
Sampson made a friendly gesture, pointing to one of the steps.
"I didn't come for a social," said Roscoe.
"I'll say you didn't.
You sure don't look like you're ready to party with me,
unless you're going to a Ragpicker's Ball."

Sampson just won round two!

In case I didn't tell you,
Sampson is a great sounder.
He can out talk any body, including his mother.

"You're asking for it, Sampson!" Roscoe said.
"I can't be bothered exchanging knocks with a nut like you."
"You can't what?" said Sampson.
He was getting interested now for sure.
"This top in my hand says I'm the top cat around here."

"No good!" Sampson shook his head.
He smiled now, more relaxed.
"The sun has created a major turbulence in your head, jazz.
In other words, I think, you're nuts."

"Challenge," shouted Roscoe throwing down his handkerchief.

By now Sampson was laughing so hard
he could hardly bend to pick up the handkerchief to accept the challenge.
But he did.

"We'll meet at the end of the week," he said.

"Why not now, Sampson? Afraid?"

"Not at all, friend, not at all.
I need a day or two to get my top oiled up.
I'm going to spin you silly."

Naturally news flashed along the block faster than thunder.
Even groups from other turfs wanted to see this show.
There was going to be such a crowd
that the contest was set for Saturday in the school yard.

No one saw Sampson for the next few days, except at school.
He wasn't mixing with us in the afternoon like he usually did,
so word was out that he was really frightened.
But now, in thinking it all over,
Roscoe was his own publicity man
and he was the one who spread the rumor
that Sampson had a case of the shakes.

Things didn't rest right with me.
Something funny was going on.
I was sure of it.

Now, just by chance, I happened to be up on the roof,
peeking down into the alley one day
when I discovered exactly why I had some not-too-nice suspicions
about Roscoe.
You see, Roscoe was going all over showing off his top.
He wouldn't let anybody hold it.
In fact, he never really let anybody get too close to it.
But every one in a while,
he'd spin it and boy what a noise it would make.

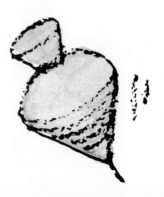

As I was saying,
I happened to be up on the roof when I looked down
and there was Roscoe.
I suspected that he was up to something,
since Roscoe is the kind who is always into one action or another.
Roscoe had something over his head
that looked like a wedding veil.
Some way out space gloves ran up the length of his arms.
Then, I saw him uncap the top.
Believe me, I was so shocked by what I saw
that I almost fell three stories down on top of Roscoe's head.
Roscoe had some bees in that top.
That was a wild insurance policy.
In a minute, I had this deal completely figured.
Roscoe's top couldn't fail.
The bees would give his top good balance at all times.

This was good information to have.
But I wasn't running snitching to Sampson.
I mean, we weren't tight or anything like that.

But most important of all,
my personality is not inclined toward snitching.

The big day came on strong.
At school, everybody was touchy.
As much as the kids disliked Roscoe,
they tended to dislike Sampson even more
because he was just too good at everything.
Most of the kids, even the ones who liked Sampson,
were waiting for him to be put down just once.

After school, we pushed into the school yard.
In about fifteen minutes,
kids from other turfs started falling in on bikes,
box car scooters and on their left and right.
Sampson was in no hurry.
He looked so calm that I got the shakes for him.
Roscoe was running around,
jumping bad with everyone who said anything not to his liking.
I couldn't figure out what he had to be so nervous about,
since in my book, he had a sure thing going for him.
I got up close to him so that I could view him and his top
from all angles.

I could see tiny air holes that fit right in with the design of the top
and also there to keep the bees from getting smothered.

Now there are established rules for top men.
In order to be top cat
you've got to be able to do some tricks with the top.
My favorite is spinning the top out gently
and then even more gently
bringing it up in the palm of my hand.
That trick is like something else.

Roscoe and Sampson started the tricks.
First one and then the other.
The first few tricks were nothing.
But things got more exciting as they moved along.
The points were pretty even.

Then came sneaker tip.
The tops spun out and Roscoe was the first
to get his top to climb up on the toe of his shoe.
Sampson was still trying, but Roscoe was clean.
You could have heard a pin drop.

Roscoe was now ahead by ten points.
"Champ of Everything, Failure at Nothing"
appeared to be in the process of losing his title.

Next came transfer.
The top spins out and is picked up with the right hand,
spun off to the left hand,
then returned to the ground.
Roscoe ran away with that gag, too.
All the kids started clapping with great enthusiasm.
Roscoe was their boy.
Sampson was working out, but he kept coming in second.

Deep down, the information I had stored was trying to surface.
I knew Roscoe wasn't doing right,
but, like other kids, I felt Sampson needed to be brought down,
if just this once.

The last trick was on now
and Sampson broke into some bad action.
He let his top spin out
and when it was spinning real good,
he did a lift-off on the middle finger,
then to the back of his right hand
right up to his shoulder.
Then leaning back like some kind of circus acrobat,
he made that top dance right on down his chest,
down to his right leg
and off the top of his sneaker back onto the ground.

You may say it sounds like nothing,
but the trick is to try it.
Sampson was setting a wild pace now.
And the kids, well strange as it seemed,
suddenly started rooting for Sampson.

Roscoe didn't seem the least bit worried by Sampson's finale.
I guess, he was planning some bad action of his own.
Well, he set that top spinning.
Sampson was standing over on the side, watching.
The top was spinning and humming real pretty.
Yet, nobody seemed to notice that the hum was getting louder and louder.
I kind of figured that those bees were pretty dizzy by now.
Then Roscoe goes into lift-off.
That's the trick that Sampson had just performed,
only he was doing it in reverse.
It sure was a pretty sight to see that top,
working up his right leg.
Then he leaned back so that it would spin on his chest.
It was then that Roscoe's action really got bad
and how bad it was you should only know.

Sampson was getting a wild pace now.

Then Roscoe goes into lift-off.

One minute the top was spinning on his chest
up by his shirt collar
and the next minute it was gone.
You know, like first you see it now you don't.
I figured this was part of what Roscoe was putting down.
Suddenly he leaps.
Well, I must say I had never seen top action like this before.
His sneakers came down on the school yard cement
and Roscoe was moving like two Hula dancers stuck in a hoop.
The cat was all over the place at once.
Suddenly I saw one of those bees stagger out of Roscoe's shirt
and fall to the ground.
Well the kids were shocked.
Then some of them took a real close look at Roscoe and took off,
trying to avoid such drastic bad action.
And all this time,
Sampson just stood on the side watching.

Roscoe finally collapsed.
It was then that Sampson picked him up,
slung him over his shoulder and took him home.

Well this tale could go on.
I could tell you about the pain of Roscoe's hospitalization
and recuperation.
I could tell you about Sampson's silence on the entire situation.
But I think you can figure all these things out for yourself.
The important thing of all of this is
that we learned an important lesson.
In fact this tale was so good we learned a couple of lessons.
First of all,
if you know a boaster who can do all he claims,
don't try to count him out with a trick.
Then, too, bees hive in trees, not in tops—
unless you've got a guaranteed stay-on top on your top.

You know, like first you see it now you don't.

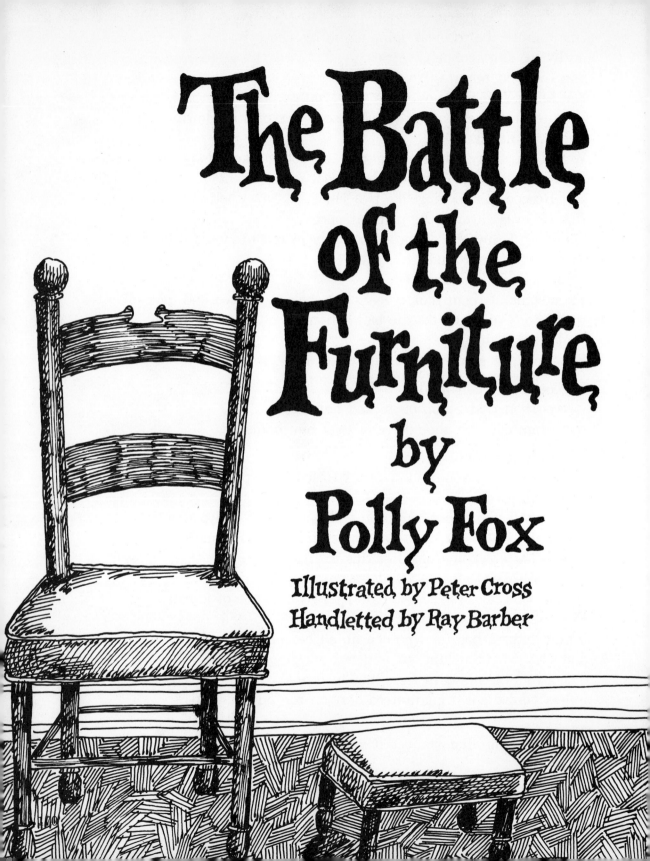

The Battle of the Furniture
by
Polly Fox

Illustrated by Peter Cross
Handletted by Ray Barber

Carol suddenly felt very much alone.
Not that she was afraid. It was just that she
had never been at home all alone before.
"I believe I'll call Grandma", Carol said aloud.
The sound of her voice in the quiet house made her
jump a little. She went to the phone and dialed. The
phone clicked
Strangely.

Carol was surprised. "Hello?" "Hello yourself!" "Grandma?" Carol asked timidly. "Do I look like your grandmother?" "I'm sure I don't know," said Carol. "I can't see you." "Well use your eyes, silly, I'm right in front of your face." "Who am I talking to?" Carol's voice quavered. "The telephone, of course. Who do you think I am, the toaster?" "I just never knew you could talk!" "Certainly I can talk. I hope you are worth talking to." Well for goodness sake!" Carol sank down in a chair. She thought for a moment. It was hard to know what to say to a telephone. "Do all phones talk, or are you especially clever?" "Yes." "Yes what?"

"Watch who you're kicking!" a new voice demanded.

"What!" Carol gasped.

"I don't mind you sitting on my lap, but would you please stop kicking my shin."

"Oh my!" cried Carol as she jumped up and stared at the chair. "Do you talk too?"

"Of course I talk. Do you think the phone is the only bright one around here?"

"Why no! I'm afraid I'm just a little confused. Why have you kept quiet all this time, and why are you talking to me now?"

"Shall we tell her?" the telephone asked.

"We'll have to," the end table agreed.

"But what can she do?" asked the fancy vase. "She's only a girl."

"Tell her," urged the carpet.

"Tell me what?" Carol was almost in tears.

"Well, the trouble is, umbrella was leaning out on the porch yesterday when he overheard two men talking. They were planning a robbery."

"Oh?" Carol said.

"A robbery of this house!"

"Oh no!" she gasped.

"They are planning to steal all of us and anything else they can find. Tonight!"

"What shall we do?" Carol cried.

"We thought you might call the police," a candlestick suggested.

"Of course," Carol agreed "But what will I say? I can't tell them my umbrella overheard a robbery being planned. They won't believe me."

"It's too late anyway," whispered the door. "They're turning my knob right now!"

175

"Oh no!"

Carol gasped.

"Quick, Carol, hide behind me!" the couch urged. Carol ducked behind the couch just as the door quietly opened. Robber Number One put his head in, looked all around and whispered,

"It's clear."

In he tiptoed with his partner. "Shh!" Number One cautioned.

"Can you trip them?" Carol whispered to the carpet.

"Of course," the carpet said.

"What about you?" she whispered to the lamp. "Can you give them a shock?"

"Yes!" said the lamp very quietly.

"And can you pinch their fingers?" Carol whispered to the closet door. "Just watch me!" the door replied.

Every piece of furniture began planning what to do. The robbers now were in the center of the room.

The vase on the mantle was the first to strike. It threw itself from its perch and cracked Number One over the head, shattering into pieces.

"Ouch!" he shouted.

"Shut up, you fool," said Number Two. "And don't be so clumsy!"

"This is war!" breathed the couch.

"Let's try that closet," suggested Robber One, rubbing the bump on his head.

The two men moved to the closet and opened the door, and ~ BANG! ~ the door swung shut, catching a finger.

"Owwwwww!" shouted Number Two.

"Shut up, fool!" his partner said.

"Well, did you see that!"

"Sure, sure," said Robber One as he began opening the drawers of the desk. "Youch!" he screamed as the drawer slammed shut on his hand. "Say, what's going on?" Suddenly the carpet began rolling.

"Help!" the men shouted as they toppled to the floor.

"Charge!" rumbled the couch. All the furniture converged on the enemy, crashing, banging, hitting, bumping, slugging! The end tables kicked with their sharp little legs. The rocking chair rocked on their fingers and toes.

"Try to steal us, will you!" shouted the potted plant, as it threw clods of dirt.

"We'll teach you!" rattled the grandfather clock, but of course he was too old to join the battle.

"Let's get out of here!" shouted Robber One.

"I'm with you!" cried his partner, and the two ran out the door and crashed in a heap at the bottom of the porch steps.

"Whew!" gasped Carol, tearfully. "Thank you so much. You were wonderful!"

"Don't mention it," answered the phone. "You gave us the idea."

"Yes! Thank you, Carol!" shouted all the furniture.

"Here comes your grandmother, Carol," the door warned.

"Oh no! Look at this mess!"

"Quick, let's get cleaned up!" the carpet shouted.

The furniture began to straighten itself up and hurried back to their usual places. The couch fluffed his cushions, the end tables smoothed their doiles, the broom began to sweep, and the carpet lifted his corner just in time for the dirt to be swept underneath. Broom rushed back to the closet and closed the door just as Grandmother entered.

"Hello, dear, are you all alone?" Grandma asked.

"I guess you might say that," Carol answered.
"O look, this vase is broken!" Grandmother
bent down to pick up the pieces.

"Yes, I know," said Carol. "It was an accident."

"Never mind," said Grandma. "I didn't like
that vase anyway."

"Oh, I think it was a wonderful vase," Carol
murmured as she helped pick up the pieces.

The grandfather clock suddenly began to
toll ten minutes before the hour.

"Now what's wrong with that clock?"
Grandmother asked. "It's chiming is off!"

Carol didn't answer, but she knew the
clock was saluting the fallen hero.

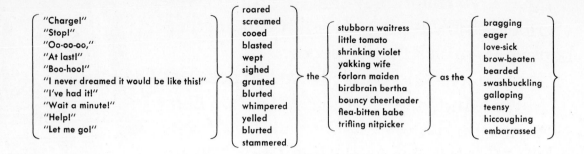

"Charge!" / "Stop!" / "Oo-oo-oo," / "At last!" / "Boo-hoo!" / "I never dreamed it would be like this!" / "I've had it!" / "Wait a minute!" / "Help!" / "Let me go!"

roared / screamed / cooed / blasted / wept / sighed / grunted / blurted / whimpered / yelled / blurted / stammered

the

stubborn waitress / little tomato / shrinking violet / yakking wife / forlorn maiden / birdbrain bertha / bouncy cheerleader / flea-bitten babe / trifling nitpicker

as the

bragging / eager / love-sick / brow-beaten / bearded / swashbuckling / galloping / teensy / hiccoughing / embarrassed

suitor / lover / Romeo / husband / villain / sailor / halfback / tuba player

pulled / stroked / accepted / ducked / slapped / kissed / met / tweaked

her

frozen / frizzled / adoring / flying / rosy / wicked / stilted / drooping

nose / wig / gaze / left / cheek / tresses / smile / eyelashes

and

crooned / thrust / slipped / dropped / threw / popped / dumped / forced

his

corny / mushy / weekly / handsome / silly

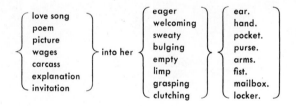

love song / poem / picture / wages / carcass / explanation / invitation

into her

eager / welcoming / sweaty / bulging / empty / limp / grasping / clutching

ear. / hand. / pocket. / purse. / arms. / fist. / mailbox. / locker.

Creative Writing Made Easy

PAINTING BY SAMUEL MAITIN

Answers to Hockey I.Q. Test (page 138)

1. Clint Benedict,
Montreal Maroons in 1930.
2. Gordie Howe,
Detroit Red Wings,
786 in 25 seasons.
3. Bobby Orr,
Boston Bruins, 1970-71.
4. Ken Dryden,
Montreal Canadiens.
5. Bill Masterton,
Minnesota North Stars, in 1968.
6. Tony Esposito,
Chicago Black Hawks,
15 shutouts, 1969-70.
7. Bobby Orr, Boston Bruins.
8. Bobby Hull, Winnipeg Jets.
9. Gil Perreault, Buffalo Sabres.
10. Keith Magnuson,
Chicago Black Hawks,
291 minutes, 1970-71.
11. Serge Savard,
Montreal Canadiens.
12. Andy Hebenton,
New York Rangers
and Boston Bruins, 630 games.
13. 200 feet long and 85 feet wide.

To Destiny

Bear down lightly,
O my load,
Bear down lightly
As the boat touches the water;
Bear down lightly,
O my load
For my boat is near to sinking;
Bear light,
And I will make offerings
To the Master of Destiny.

A SONG FROM DAHOMEY

THE WITCH DOCTOR BY HEZBON OWITI

HOME FROM THE SEA   WOODCUTS BY ADEBISI FABUNMI

EMPTY STAR

1 In the beginning
God created the heaven and the earth.
2 And the earth was without form, and void;
and darkness was upon the face of the deep.
And the Spirit of God moved
upon the face of the waters.
3 And God said,
Let there be light:
and there was light.
4 And God saw the light,
that it was good:
and God divided the light from the darkness.
5 And God called the light Day,
and the darkness he called Night.
And the evening and the morning
were the first day.

THE FIRST DAY

The Story
of
the Creation

AS TOLD IN THE BOOK OF GENESIS

"NEOLITHIC AFTERNOON" BY MAYNARD DIXON

"WATERING HOLE" BY CECIL SMITH

6 And God said,
Let there be a firmament in the midst of the waters,
and let it divide the waters from the waters.
7 And God made the firmament,
and divided the waters which were under the firmament
from the waters which were above the firmament:
and it was so.
8 And God called the firmament Heaven.
And the evening
and the morning
were the second day.   *THE SECOND DAY*

The Story
of
the Creation

AS TOLD IN THE BOOK OF GENESIS

"WHITE MESA" BY MAYNARD DIXON

9 And God said,
Let the waters under the heaven
be gathered together unto one place,
and let the dry land appear:
and it was so.
10 And God called the dry land Earth;
and the gathering together of the waters
called he Seas:
and God saw that it was good.
11 And God said,
Let the earth bring forth grass,
the herb yielding seed,
and the fruit tree yielding fruit after his kind,
whose seed is in itself, upon the earth:
and it was so.
12 And the earth brought forth grass,
and herb yielding seed after his kind,
and the tree yielding fruit,
whose seed was in itself, after his kind:
and God saw that it was good.
13 And the evening
and the morning
were the third day.

THE THIRD DAY

The Story
of
the Creation

AS TOLD IN THE BOOK OF GENESIS

14 And God said,
Let there be lights in the firmament of the heaven
to divide the day from the night;
and let them be for signs,
and for seasons,
and for days,
and years:
15 And let them be for lights in the firmament of the heaven
to give light upon the earth:
and it was so.
16 And God made two great lights;
the greater light to rule the day,
and the lesser light to rule the night:
he made the stars also.
17 And God set them in the firmament of the heaven
to give light upon the earth,
18 And to the rule over the day and over the night,
and to divide the light from the darkness:
and God saw that it was good.
19 And the evening
and the morning
were the fourth day.

THE FOURTH DAY

The Story
of
the Creation

AS TOLD IN THE BOOK OF GENESIS

"INDIAN SCOUT" BY MAYNARD DIXON

"LONESOME LAND" BY CECIL SMITH

20 And God said,
Let the waters bring forth abundantly
the moving creature that hath life,
and fowl that may fly above the earth
in the open firmament of heaven.
21 And God created great whales,
and every living creature that moveth,
which the waters brought forth abundantly,
after their kind,
and every winged fowl after his kind:
and God saw that it was good.
22 And God blessed them, saying,
Be fruitful, and multiply,
and fill the waters in the seas,
and let fowl multiply in the earth.
23 And the evening
and the morning
were the fifth day.

THE FIFTH DAY

The Story
of
the Creation

AS TOLD IN THE BOOK OF GENESIS

24 And God said,
Let the earth bring forth the living creature after his kind,
cattle, and creeping thing, and beast of the earth after his kind:
and it was so.

25 And God made the beast of the earth after his kind,
and cattle after their kind,
and every thing that creepeth upon the earth after his kind:
and God saw that it was good.

26 And God said,
Let us make man in our image, after our likeness:
and let them have dominion over the fish of the sea,
and over the fowl of the air, and over the cattle, and over all the earth,
and over every creeping thing that creepeth upon the earth.

27 So God created man in his own image,
in the image of God created he him; male and female created he them.

28 And God blessed them,
and God said unto them,
Be fruitful, and multiply, and replenish the earth, and subdue it:
and have dominion over the fish of the sea, and over the fowl of the air,
and over every living thing that moveth upon the earth.

29 And God said,
Behold, I have given you every herb bearing seed,
which is upon the face of all the earth, and every tree,
in the which is the fruit of a tree yielding seed;
to you it shall be for meat.

30 And to every beast of the earth,
and to every fowl of the air,
and to every thing
that creepeth upon the earth,
wherein there is life,
I have given every green herb for meat:
and it was so.

31 And God saw every thing
that he had made,
and, behold, it was very good.
And the evening and the morning
were the sixth day.

THE SIXTH DAY

The Story
of
the Creation

AS TOLD IN THE BOOK OF GENESIS

"CANYON DEL MUERTO" BY MAYNARD DIXON

"MYSTERY STONE" BY MAYNARD DIXON

The Story
of
the Creation

AS TOLD IN THE BOOK OF GENESIS

1 Thus the heavens and the earth were finished,
and all the host of them.
2 And on the seventh day
God ended his work which he had made;
and he rested on the seventh day from all his work
which he had made.
3 And God blessed the seventh day,
and sanctified it:
because that in it he had rested from all his work
which God created and made.

DE PESSENTS

Verse and pictures by John R. Dunn

EEN DE FUL VEN YECK VROST GOMMINK
    HALL DE PESSENTS STUT TO RON
SES VON HROOSTER, "VE PE BRACKTICE
    VOR DEM SCHMOES VAT PENG DE GON."

BRETTY ZOON DE GONFIELD VILLINK
    VIT DEES NEEMRUTS EN TER TOK
"HON YOU MUCK," SES POSS KUY PESSENT,
    "LEST VON TO DE ZLEW ES HOK."

EEN DE ZLEW DE MUSTER HOLDINK
    HALLES BRESANT, HALL PUT VUN
SES DE POSS, "LAT DEES PE LESSIN,
    DAT KUY GUNG VAKE HUP GUN."

EEN DE GONFIELD ZLEEPIN PEAUTY
    VAKIN VIT VON RONINK YUMP
TOK ES LENDIN HON DAIL VEDDERS
    VEET VON YOWLIN HOPPIN GLUMP.

HALL DE SOOTERS PINGIN PANGIN
    PE PEES VLYING HALL HABOUT
ZOM ES PUPIN VON DE NEEMRUTS
    VERE DE PENTS ES GINDA ZSTOUT.

HALL DEES SCHMOES KENT HEET DE BUN DOR
    NUR DE ZQUAKIN YUMPIN BUT
DEN VON NEEMRUT DREEP HON GONSTUK
    GON KO PENG EN ZLEEPER SHUT.

GOMS DE MORAL SES DE POSS KUY,
    "VEN EETS DIME VOR RONINK YET,
DUNT PE ZNEAKIN VORTY VEENKS
    HOR YOU ES GUNG TO VAKE HUP DET."

ASTROLOGICAL FAMILIES

DRAWINGS BY PETER MAX

ARIES   **MARCH 21-APRIL 20**

I AM

Aries is the sign of the Ram and a cardinal fiery sign which makes us energetic, impulsive and enthusiastic. Aries are ruled by the planet Mars and rule the head of man. I am head-strong, a natural fighter and the pioneer of the zodiac. I love to travel and am known for my courage. Compatible signs are Sagittarius and Leo.

Color—Red   Sign—Ram

peter max ©

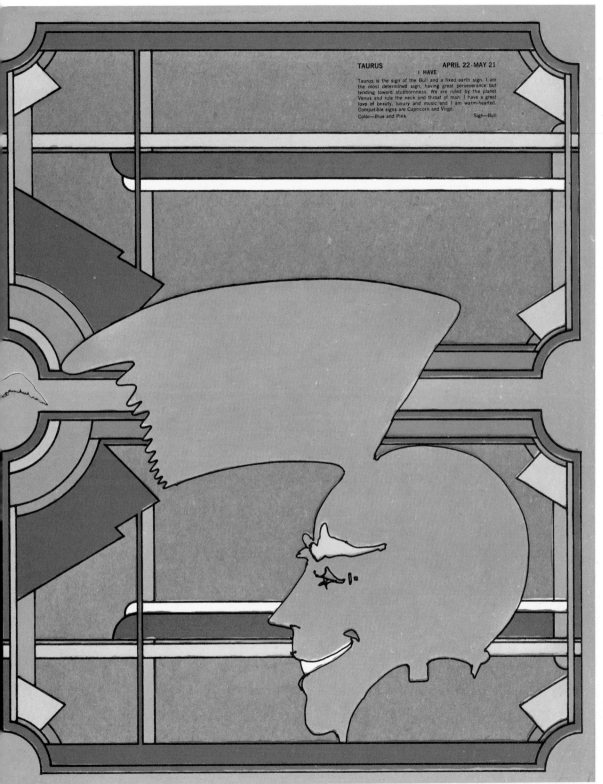

TAURUS   APRIL 22-MAY 21
                     I HAVE
Taurus is the sign of the Bull and a fixed earth sign. I am
the most determined sign, having great perseverance but
tending toward stubbornness. We are ruled by the planet
Venus and rule the neck and throat of man. I have a great
love of beauty, luxury and music and I am warm-hearted.
Compatible signs are Capricorn and Virgo.
Color—Blue and Pink   Sign—Bull

205

GEMINI   **MAY 22-JUNE 21**
                    I THINK
Gemini is the sign of the Twins and a mutable air sign. I am
versatile, clever and sometimes controversial. I am ruled by
the planet Mercury and I rule the shoulders, arms and hands
of man. I am exuberant and energetic with a tendency towards
free expression. Compatible signs are Aquarius and Libra.
Color—Yellow   Sign—Twins

peter max©

207

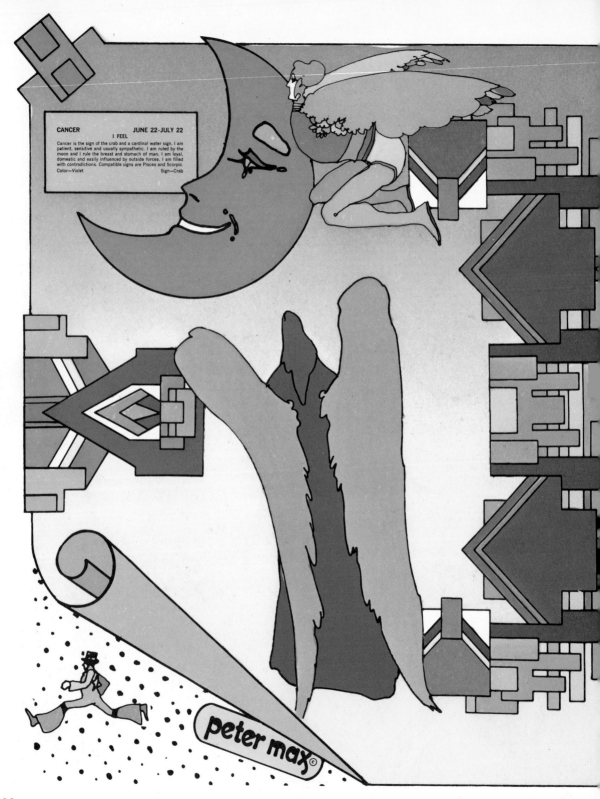

CANCER

I FEEL

JUNE 22-JULY 22

Cancer is the sign of the crab and a cardinal water sign. I am patient, sensitive and usually sympathetic. I am ruled by the moon and I rule the breast and stomach of man. I am loyal, domestic and easily influenced by outside forces. I am filled with contradictions. Compatible signs are Pisces and Scorpio.

Color—Violet   Sign—Crab

peter max ©

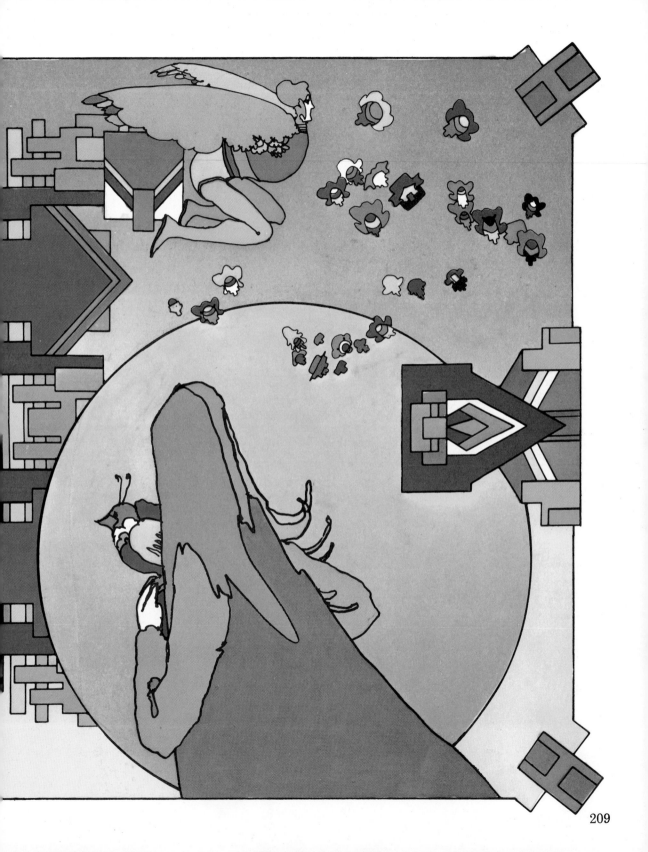

LEO **JULY 23-AUGUST 23**
I WILL

Leo is the sign of the Lion and a fixed fire sign. I am proud, energetic and sometimes authoritative. I am ruled by the sun and I rule the heart and back of man. I am generous, romantic and creative. Love is of paramount importance. Compatible signs are Sagittarius and Aries.

Color—Orange Sign—Leo

peter max ©

VIRGO   **AUGUST 24-SEPTEMBER 23**
I ANALYZE

Virgo is the sign of the Virgin and a mutable earth sign. I am intelligent, industrious and methodical. I am ruled by Mercury and I rule the intestines (digestive system) of man. I am extremely conscientious but tend to talk a lot. I always do my part. Compatible signs are Capricorn and Taurus.

Color—Navy Blue and Grey   Sign—Virgin

peter max ©

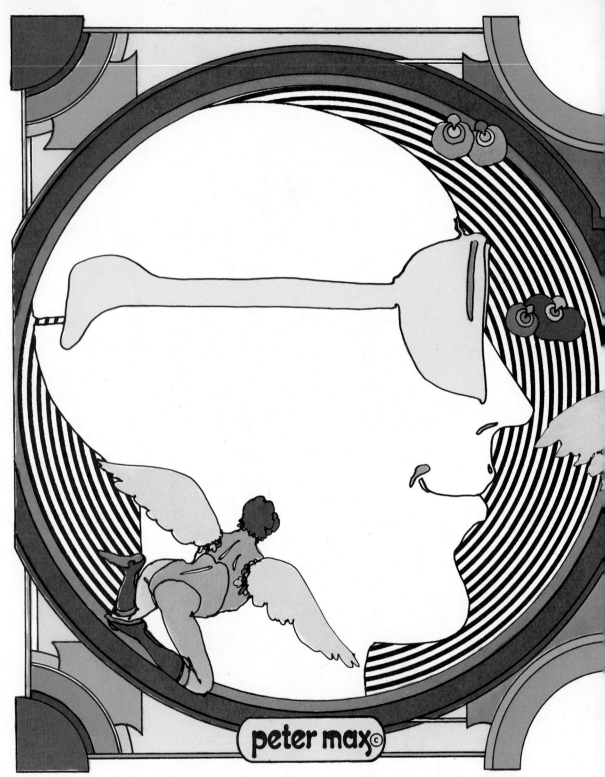

peter max©

214

LIBRA **SEPTEMBER 24-OCTOBER 23**
I BALANCE

Libra is the sign of the scale and a cardinal air sign. I am just, honest and painstaking. I am interested in details. Ruled by Venus, I rule the kidneys of man. I am artistic, affectionate and sympathetic. I long for justice, love, and beauty. Compatible signs are Aquarius and Gemini.
Color—Indigo and Blue   Sign—Scale

SCORPIO   OCTOBER 24-NOVEMBER 22
                        I DESIRE

Scorpio is the sign of the scorpion and a fixed water sign.
I am independent, determined and energetic, I can become
passionate and sensual and develop strong attachments. I
am ruled by Mars and I rule the reproductive organs of man.
I search for a union of the practical with the mystical. Compatible signs are Cancer and Pisces.
Color—Deep Red and Black   Sign—Scorpion

peter max©

216

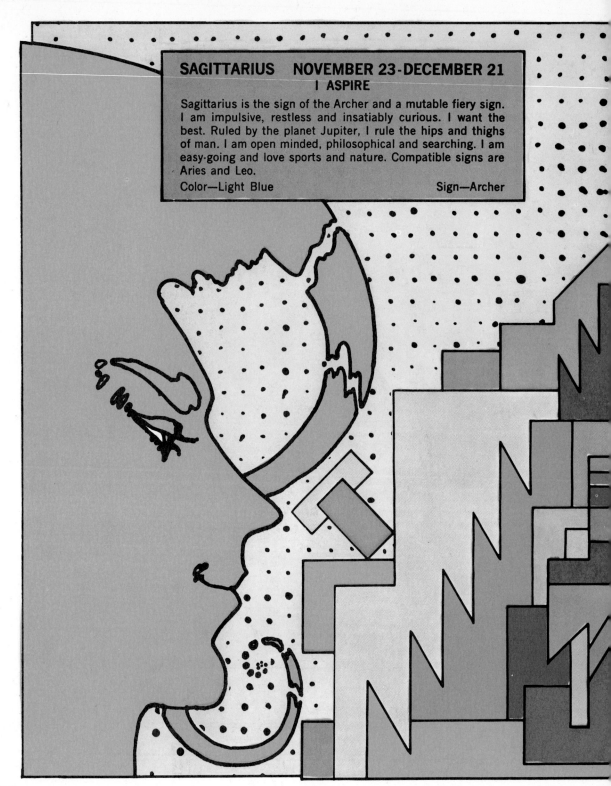

SAGITTARIUS   NOVEMBER 23-DECEMBER 21
I ASPIRE

Sagittarius is the sign of the Archer and a mutable fiery sign.
I am impulsive, restless and insatiably curious. I want the
best. Ruled by the planet Jupiter, I rule the hips and thighs
of man. I am open minded, philosophical and searching. I am
easy-going and love sports and nature. Compatible signs are
Aries and Leo.

Color—Light Blue   Sign—Archer

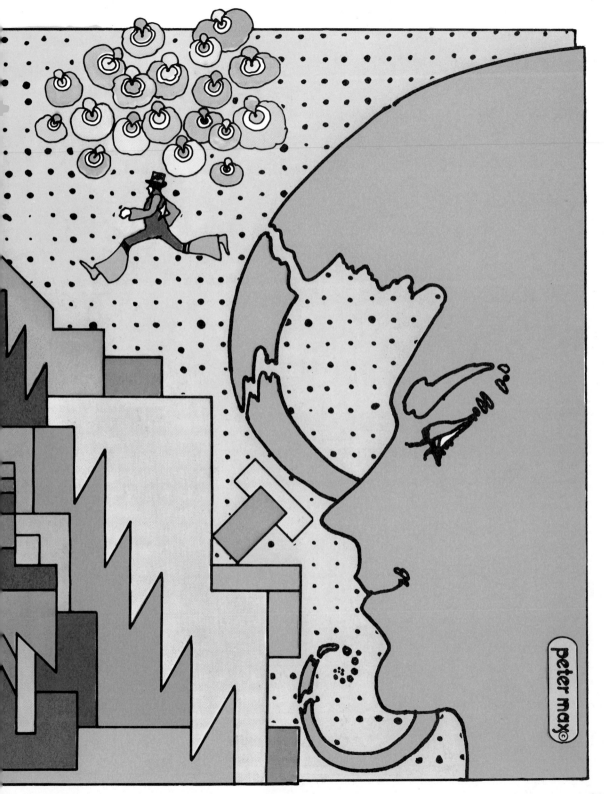

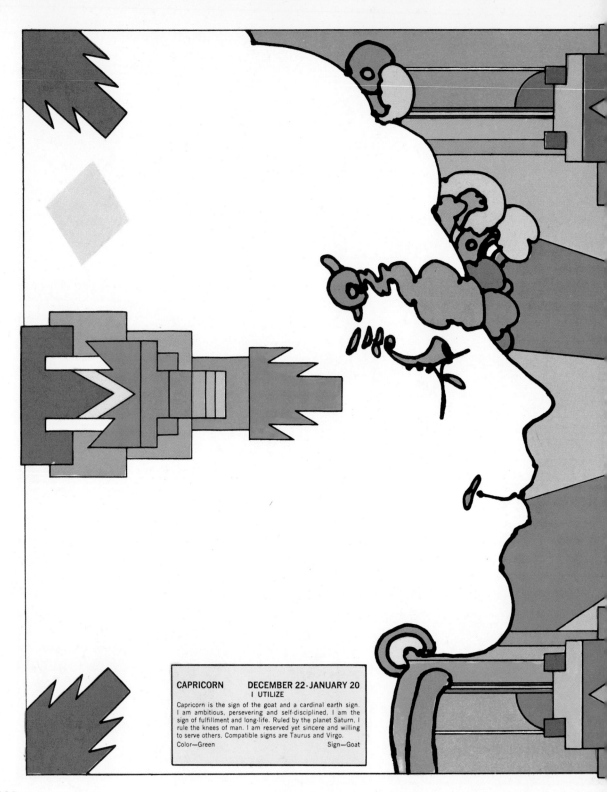

CAPRICORN   DECEMBER 22-JANUARY 20
I UTILIZE

Capricorn is the sign of the goat and a cardinal earth sign.
I am ambitious, persevering and self-disciplined. I am the
sign of fulfillment and long-life. Ruled by the planet Saturn, I
rule the knees of man. I am reserved yet sincere and willing
to serve others. Compatible signs are Taurus and Virgo.
Color—Green   Sign—Goat

221

AQUARIUS JANUARY 21-FEBRUARY 19
I KNOW

Aquarius is the sign of the water bearer and a fixed air sign. I am honest, broadminded and tend to be idealistic. I am searching for truth. Ruled by the planet Uranus, I rule the ankles of man. I am involved in the metaphysical and the universal. I view life with detachment, yet I try to help others always. Compatible signs are Libra and Gemini.
Color—Electric Blue Sign—Water Bearer

peter max©

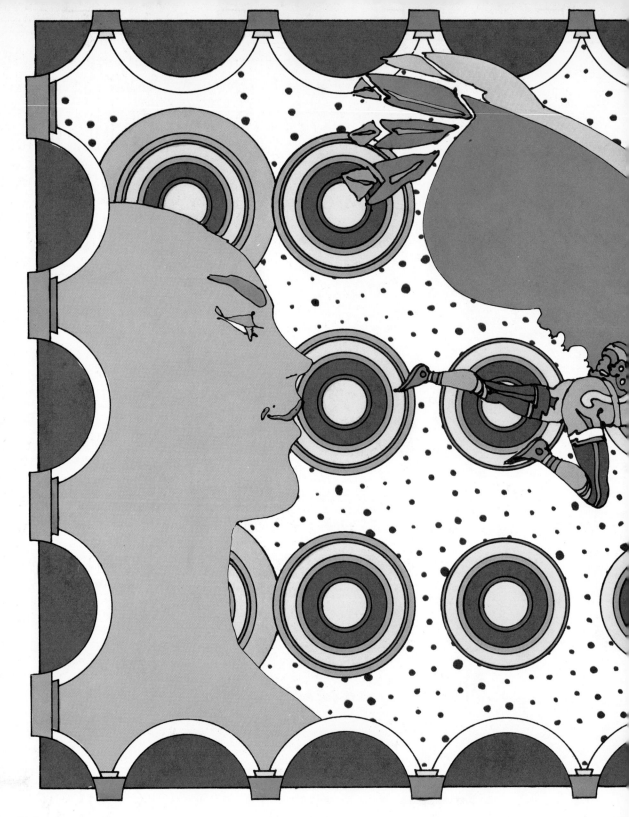

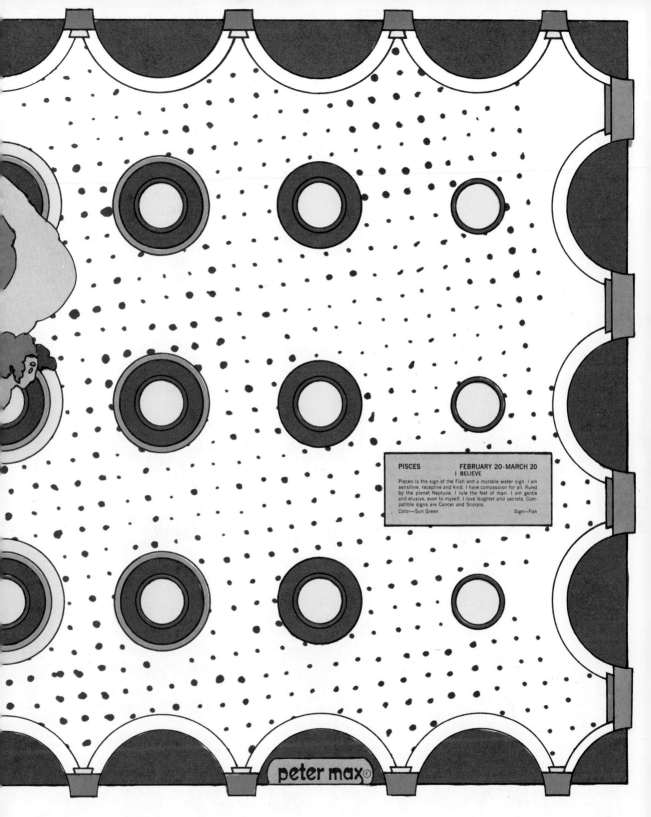

PISCES   **FEBRUARY 20-MARCH 20**
I BELIEVE

Pisces is the sign of the Fish and a mutable water sign. I am sensitive, receptive and kind. I have compassion for all. Ruled by the planet Neptune. I rule the feet of man. I am gentle and elusive, even to myself. I love laughter and secrets. Compatible signs are Cancer and Scorpio.

Color—Sun Green   Sign—Fish

peter max ©

THE KING'S

SCULPTORS AND SIGNPAINTER LOCAL NO V

LEGS

A STORY BY RICHARD HUGHES, ART BY PETER LIPPMAN

There was once a farmer who got tired of farming,
so he thought he would go to the town
and start an inn.
When he got there he found
that there were two inns already in the town.
One was called *The King's Head*,
and one was called *The King's Arms*.
"Very well," he said, "I shall call my inn
The King's Legs."

Now this turned out very well.
Nobody had ever heard of an inn
being called *The King's Legs* before,
so strangers used to come in,
out of curiosity,
to ask why on earth
the inn had such a strange name.
Then, of course, they had at least to buy
something to drink and a bite to eat,
and sometimes they stayed the night
so as to be able to use note paper
with such a lovely address
when writing to their friends.
And so *The King's Legs* inn became
the most prosperous in the town,
and the new innkeeper got rich
and the old innkeepers began to get poor.

So the old innkeepers put their heads together
and wondered what was the reason.

"I know," said the landlord of *The King's Arms.*
"It is because he has got such a funny name for his inn.
I'm going to change the name of mine."

So he decided to call his inn
      The King's Stomach;
and he took down the old sign
to get a new picture painted.
"Mind you, make it a big one,"
he said to the sign-painter,
"or else it won't look royal"—
though, as a matter of fact,
the King of that country was not particularly fat at all.

Then he hung up the new sign.
But what happened was not at all what he expected.

Some courtiers of the King happened
to be traveling that way;
and when they saw the sign,
they were very angry and shocked.

"WHAT!" they cried.
"The impudent creature!
Fancy calling *that* great fat stomach the King's!
As if everyone didn't know he has the

SLIMMEST

and most elegant

LITTLE

stomach
in the kingdom!"

"What shall we do?" asked one of the courtiers.
"Shall we arrest him for high treason
  and have his head cut off?"
"We might do that," said another of the courtiers.
"But on the whole, wouldn't it be more fun
  just to throw some stones through his windows?"

The others agreed; so they got off their horses
and began throwing stones through the windows
of *The King's Stomach* inn
until there wasn't a single pane of glass left unbroken.
Then they rode on.

So the landlord of *The King's Stomach*
said to the landlord of *The King's Head*,
"Well, *my* plan didn't work very well.
Have you got one?"

"Yes, I have," said the landlord of *The King's Head*,
"I have thought of a very funny idea."
He went and bought a curious sort of gilt bird
and shut it up tight in a glass case
and put a label on it,

WEATHER COCK

and put it
in the window
of his inn.

Now it wasn't long before some people came by.
"Hullo," they said,
"that's a funny thing to do,
  to keep the weather cock shut up
  in a glass case where the wind can't get at it!
  I wonder why he does that?"

So they went in to ask.

"Why do you call that funny gold bird in the glass case
  a weather cock?" they asked,
  when they had ordered something to drink.

"Because," said the landlord,
"just what it is, *whether* cock or hen,
  I can't decide."

Lots of people came in to ask the same question,
  and the innkeeper gave them all the same answer.

Now the landlord of *The King's Legs*
found all the people going back to *The King's Head*,
and himself, not getting rich any more.
So he got a large gilt egg
and went along quietly at night to *The King's Head*
and slipped the egg in the glass case
along with the bird.

Next day some people came by *The King's Head*
and asked the usual question,
"Why do you call the funny gold bird in the glass case
a weather cock?"

They were given the usual answer,
"Because, just what it is,
whether cock or hen,
I can't decide."

"But you silly old ass!" they cried out
to the innkeeper,
"anyone can see it's a hen!
Why, it's laid an egg!"

And they were so angry they took up
several big glass platters that were about
and started hitting the landlord
on the head with them.
This didn't hurt his head much because it was very hard,
but it broke all the platters,
and he went along to see his friend about it all.

"It's a funny thing," said his friend,
"but whatever we do,
it always seems to end in glass being broken."

"That means," said the other one,
"there must be some sort of magic in it all."

"Well, in that case," said the first one,
"we had better go and see the Village Witch,
and ask for her advice."

So they went to the Village Witch,
who happened also to be the Village Nurse.
"There is only one thing to be done,"
said the witch.
"We must dispose of him."

"Well, will you do it for us
if we pay you well?"
asked the innkeepers.

"Certainly," said the witch, and,
putting on her nurse's uniform,
she bicycled to *The King's Legs*.
There she found the landlord in the parlor at the back.

"Dear, dear!" she said.
"I am sorry to hear you are so ill."

"Am I?" said the landlord.
"I hadn't heard."

"Perhaps not, but *I* had!"
said the witch firmly.
"You had better go to bed."

So he went to bed,
and she nursed him a bit
and then said she would come back
the next morning to see how he was.
The next day she came in the room,
looking very sad.

"You can't think how sorry I was
when I heard you had died in the night."

"What! Died in the night!
Are you sure? Nobody told me."

"No, but they told *me!*
I'll send the undertaker around this afternoon
to measure you for your coffin."

As it happened, the undertaker was busy
that afternoon and couldn't come,
but he came the next morning.

"Good morning," said the undertaker.
"I have come to bury you."

"What?" cried the innkeeper,
 who was just as clever as the witch,
 "hadn't you heard?"

239

"Heard what?" asked the undertaker.

"Why, I was buried yesterday afternoon!
  When you didn't come,
  I got the undertaker from the next town,
  and *he* buried me."

The undertaker was very sorry at that
because he didn't like losing a job,
and there was nothing to be done
if the innkeeper had been buried already,
so he went away.

Then the innkeeper got up and dressed
and went down and started work again.

Presently the witch and the two other innkeepers
looked in, to see if he was safely buried yet.
When they saw him quite well
and working again,
they were very upset.

"Good gracious!"
"What are *you* doing here?"

"What!"
"But surely you must have heard!
I am the new landlord of *The King's Legs!*
They buried the last one yesterday afternoon,
poor chap!"

At that the two other innkeepers and the witch
were so upset that,
without saying a word,
they all ran hand in hand down the village street
to the village pond and drowned themselves.
And the landlord of *The King's Legs*
got a small paintbrush
and wrote on the bottom of his sign in red paint:

TAILS IN ORBIT

An Ol' Story Told by Bill Tremaine to
folklorist Lutie Chiles, picture by Ray Barber

Now this might be just a little rough to believe but it's the way it comes to me. Two of the neighbors down where we lived, they—each one of 'em—had an old tom cat apiece. Now they thought pretty well of 'em and they thought well of each other.

They were real good friends and this neighbor up the road, he had a big blue tom cat and this neighbor down near us, he had an old gray tom cat. They were huge animals to be cats.

Anyway, this blue cat kept 'acomin' down and tormentin' this neighbor's cat down here. He wanted to rule the roost down here and the old gray cat, he wouldn't have it that way. He wanted to defend his own place.

So about every day he'd be down here tryin' to pick a fuss. This neighbor that lived close to me, he'd always run him off and next day that old blue cat'd be down here again. The gray cat never went up the road.

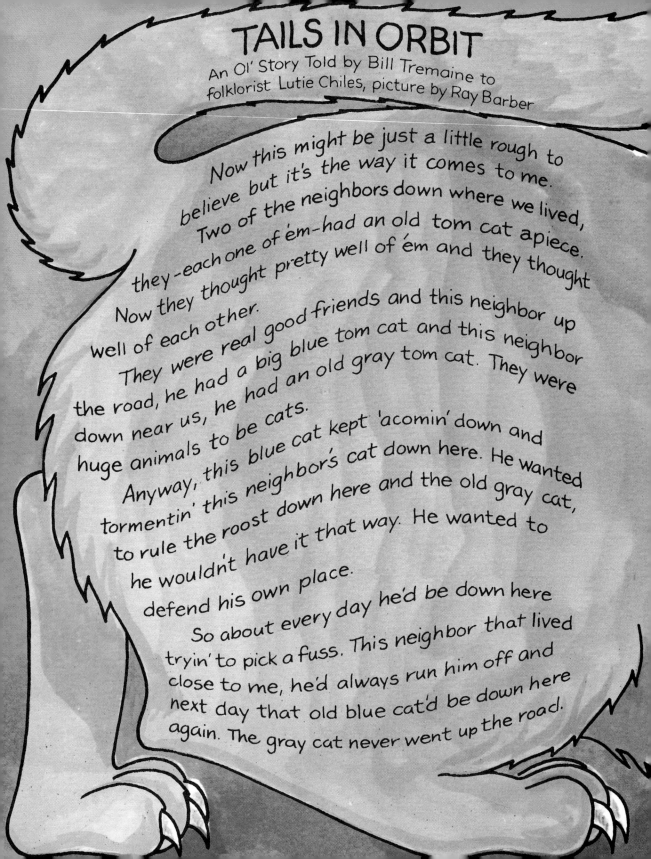

The blue one was always the trouble maker.

Anyway, they caught the old man down here in the wrong humor one day when this old blue cat showed up on his place. He decided he'd just let 'em get together and have at it and see what would happen. He'd just see which one was best. He hauled off and let 'em get at it.

So the blue one he started a slappin' and the old gray one, he slapped back. Then the blue one, he'd charge; then they'd squall. He'd go mrr-ow-rrr! Then the other'n squall marower!

Pretty soon they went together. The old blue one'd hit the gray. Then the gray'd hit him back. And then they started—just a hittin' and a climbin'—hitten' and a climbin'! Each time one'd climb, he'd get a little higher and that made somethin' for the other to hang on and they kept right on 'til they left the ground an' they went right on up into the sky.

Now the old man that was tellin' me this tale said as far as he knows, they must have gone into orbit—'cause they was never seen around here anymore.

The Maestro Plays

by Bill Martin, Jr.
handlettering by Ray Barber
pictures by Sal Murdocca

247

He plays loudly.

He plays proudly.

He plays slowly.
He plays ly.

He plays reachingly.

He plays beseechingly.

He plays flowingly glowingly

knowingly...

showingly...

goingly...

Now he is playing singingly.

He is playing ringingly, wingingly.... swingingly flingingly tingingly

faster,
faster... He plays busily. s
s s
s s
s
s

He plays DIZZILY.

HE STOPS.

HE MOPS HIS BROW.

But suddenly he's playing wildly...

HE BOWS FURIOUSLY.

He plays skippingly..

He plays sweepingly...

leapingly...

cheepingly...

faster...

faster...

He plays nippingly,
drippingly...

Zippingly...
clippingly...
pippingly...

RRRRRRiiiiiiipppppiiinngly...

The concert is over.

MAIL ORDER

by Adam Arthur,
drawings by Peter Lippman

It all began
when my son sent away
for a packet of monsters
he read about in the comic books.
Supposedly,
all you had to do
was put them in the special aquarium
that was included in the package
and the monsters would just keep growing.

To my surprise,
the package of monsters arrived
only three days after he ordered it.
The monsters were a disappointment, however.
All that was in the package
was a clear plastic tank
and two little red packs of monster powder.
The tank was filled with a liquid
that looked like water.

My son was very upset
about wasting his two dollars,
but instead of trying to get his money back,
he decided to grow the monsters,
if possible.
All that was written
in the instructions was,
"Pour the monster powder into the tank
and feed the monsters
their own weight of raw meat
every day."
The instructions sounded stupid to me
and I told my son
that this was the last thing
he was going to purchase by mail.

My son put the powder into the tank
and took it up to his room.

That night at dinner,
I noticed that he saved some meat
from his plate,
which he later took to his room.

The next day he bought a huge supply
of raw hamburger meat.
Each night he carried
increasingly larger amounts to his room.

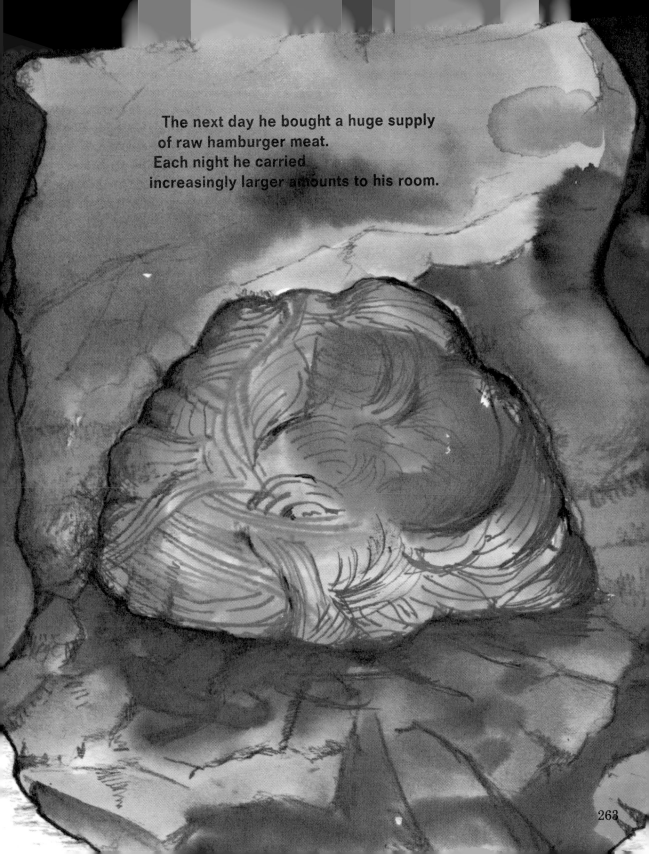

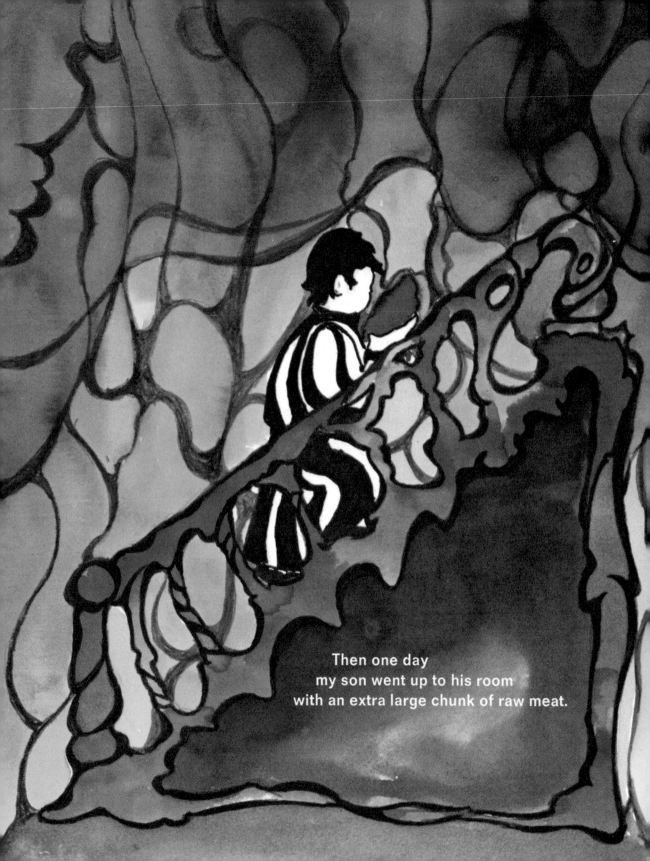

Then one day
my son went up to his room
with an extra large chunk of raw meat.

That night,
when I called him down for dinner,
he didn't come.
I sensed
that something terrible
must have happened to him.

I gathered up my courage
and walked up the stairs
that led to his room.
Slowly I opened the door
and stepped inside.

The End

SEE THE PURE
GOLD!
WHY DO PEOPLE
LOVE IT SO?
AND KEEP IT
IN A STORE
WHEN A
YELLOW
DANDELION'S

WRITTEN BY A GIRL IN WILLARD ELEMENTARY SCHOOL, EVANSTON, ILLINOIS

PURER, CHEAPER, SO MUCH MORE. THE METAL IS SO HARD AND COLD THIS LITTLE WEED'S A BETTER GOLD.

Poem and Paintings

A POEM "THE SEA WOLF" BY VIOLET MC DOUGAL,
WITH PAINTINGS BY VIC HERMAN

The fishermen say, when your catch is done
    And you're sculling in with the tide,
You must take great care that the Sea Wolf's share
    Is tossed to him overside.

They say that the Sea Wolf rides by day,
    Unseen on the crested waves,
And the sea mists rise from his cold green eyes
    When he comes from his salt sea caves.

NETWORK OF LIFE

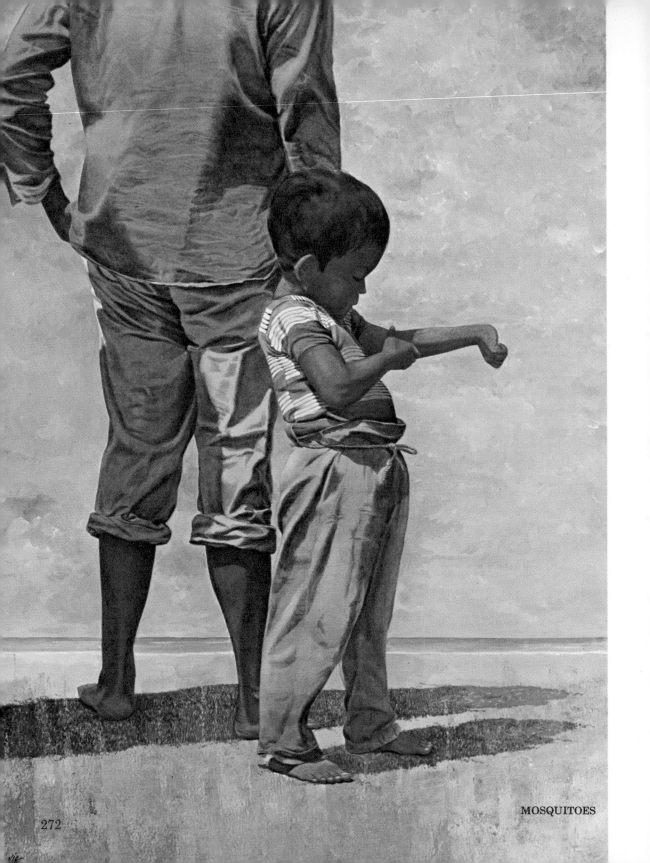

MOSQUITOES

The fishermen say, when it storms at night
 And the great seas bellow and roar,
That the Sea Wolf rides on the plunging tides,
 And you hear his howl at the door.

THE LITTLE FISHERMAN FROM BOCA DEL RIO

And you must throw open your door at once,
And fling your catch to the waves,
Till he drags his share to his cold sea lair,
Straight down to his salt sea caves.

A DAWN OF NEW HOPE

MY BUS TO TLAHUAC IS LATE

Then the storm will pass, and the still stars shine,
  In peace—so the fishermen say—
But the Sea Wolf waits by the cold Sea Gates
  For the dawn of another day.

GOD IS EVERYWHERE

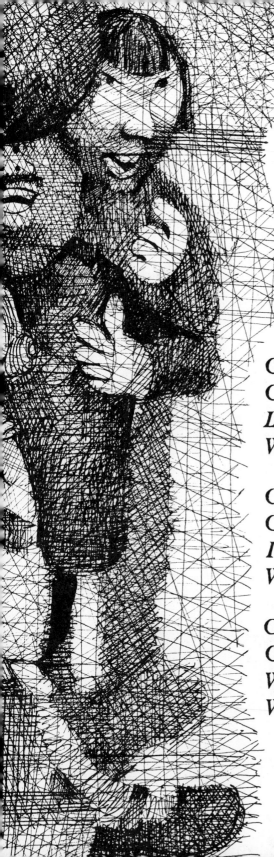

When the Saints Go Marching In

a song, adapted by Jay Arnold,
drawing by Ed Towles

Oh, *when the saints go marching in,*
Oh, *when the saints go marching in,*
Lord, *I want to be in that number,*
When the saints go marching in.

Oh, *when the saints go marching in,*
Oh, *when the saints go marching in,*
I will meet them all up in heaven,
When the saints go marching in.

Oh, *when the saints go marching in,*
Oh, *when the saints go marching in,*
We will be in line for that judgment,
When the saints go marching in.

The Tyger

A POEM BY WILLIAM BLAKE,
ILLUSTRATION BY DIANE MARTIN

Tyger! Tyger! burning bright
In the forests of the night,
What immortal hand or eye
Could frame thy fearful symmetry?

In what distant deeps or skies
Burnt the fire of thine eyes?
On what wings dare he aspire?
What the hand dare seize the fire?

And what shoulder, & what art,
Could twist the sinews of thy heart?
And when thy heart began to beat,
What dread hand? & what dread feet?

What the hammer? what the chain?
In what furnace was thy brain?
What the anvil? what dread grasp
Dare its deadly terrors clasp?

When the stars threw down their spears,
And water'd heaven with their tears,
Did he smile his work to see?
Did he who made the Lamb make thee?

Tyger! Tyger! burning bright
In the forests of the night,
What immortal hand or eye,
Dare frame thy fearful symmetry?

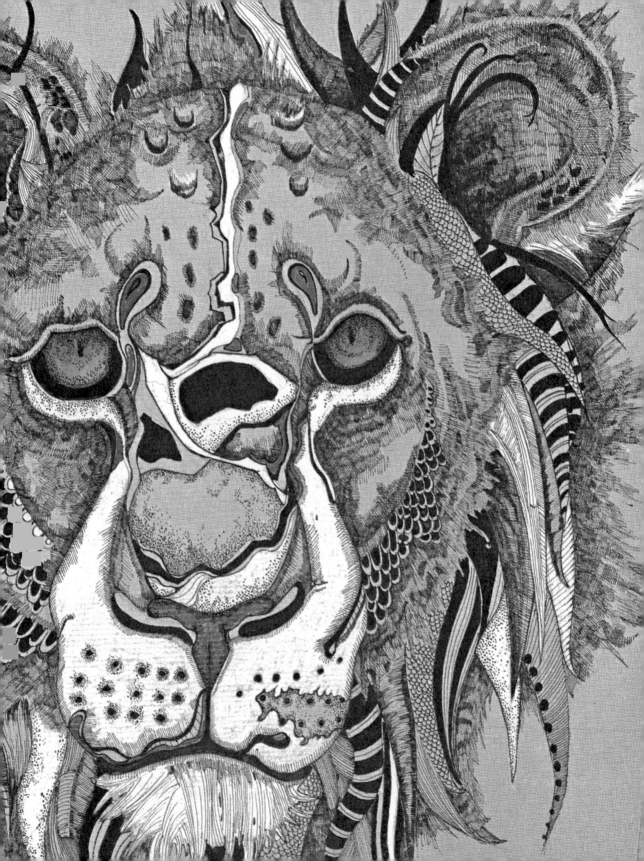

January cold desolate;

February all dripping wet;

March wind ranges;

April changes;

Birds sing in tune
To flowers of May,

And sunny June
Brings longest day;

In scorched July
The storm-clouds fly
Lightning-torn;

August bears corn,

September fruit;

In rough October
Earth must disrobe her;

Stars fall and shoot
In keen November;

And night is long
And cold is strong
In bleak December.

First Witch

Round about the cauldron go;
In the poison'd entrails throw.
Toad, that under cold stone
Days and nights has thirty-one
Swelter'd venom sleeping got,
Boil thou first i' the charmed pot.   *All*   Double, double toil and trouble;
                                                 Fire burn, and cauldron bubble.

Second Witch

Fillet of a fenny snake,
In the cauldron boil and bake;
Eye of newt and toe of frog,
Wool of bat and tongue of dog,
Adder's fork and blind-worm's sting,
Lizard's leg and howlet's wing,
For a charm of powerful trouble,
Like a hell-broth boil and bubble.   *All*   Double, double toil and trouble;
                                                 Fire burn, and cauldron bubble.

Third Witch

Scale of dragon, tooth of wolf,
Witches' mummy, maw and gulf
Of the ravin'd salt-sea shark,
Root of hemlock digged i' the dark.
Add thereto a tiger's chaudron,
For the ingredients of our cauldron. *All*   Double, double toil and trouble;
                                                 Fire burn, and cauldron bubble.

Witches' Brew

MACBETH
ACT IV SCENE I

"A recipe" by William Shakespeare,
illustration by Robert J. Lee

J.W.G.

A POEM BY
BARBARA HEINZEN

Dark Brother,
              pulling at me with all the force of a paradox
My solemn opposite,
           my brother
with your dark searching and thousand questions
        your despair
your muscle-torn fight against your despair
          wrestling with the winter of your discontent
until the whistle of spring is blown in your favor.

Dark Brother,
              pulling at me with all the force of a paradox
Saying,
      "I'll teach you on the day you are ready."
"I'll teach you to understand
    the despair
         and the fighting
    and hoping
         and hatred
           and crying inside.
"I'll teach you the runs
    in dog-tailing circles
         where escape is a word
           and a soul-busting feeling,
    but never a new life for those who can cry.
"I'll teach why winter is the hell of my brothers
    when the oil won't come
         and the sun never shines.
"All this I will teach you on the day you are ready."

Dark Brother,
    my solemn opposite,
         pulling at me with all the force of a paradox,
I am lost without you
         caught in the lace of delicate things
believing forever in the beauty of earth
    and forgetting the city which grows in cement
So take me beside you
         and teach me your life
then let me show you what I learned alone.
    Let me show you the beauty of seas
        and waves of grass in a summer heat
    let me show you the filtering leaves
        that drop star patterns on the ground beside us.

Dark Brother,
         pulling at me with all the force of a paradox,
don't let us ever
     live together
        alone.

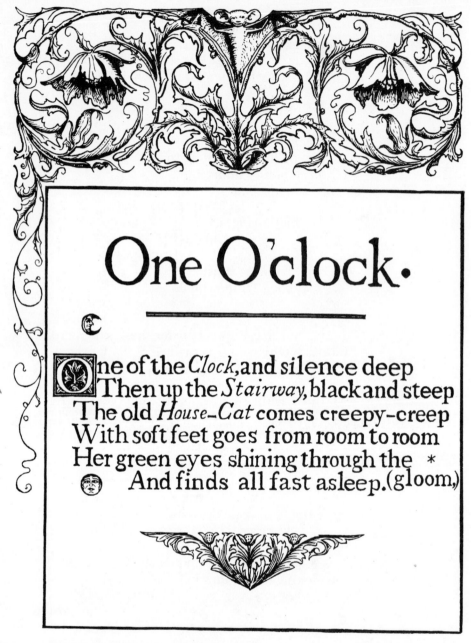

One O'clock.

One of the *Clock*, and silence deep
Then up the *Stairway*, black and steep
The old *House-Cat* comes creepy-creep
With soft feet goes from room to room
Her green eyes shining through the   *
   And finds all fast asleep. (gloom,)

A VERSE FOR EACH HOUR OF THE DAY AND NIGHT CREATES AN INTRIGUING PICTURE OF OLDEN TIMES IN RURAL ENGLAND. WRITTEN BY KATHERINE PYLE, ILLUSTRATED BY HOWARD PYLE.

The *Black Cock* crowed;
The *Moon* was bright;
The *Red Cock* answered
Through the night.

Tvvo O'clock·

Big *Gretchen*, sleeping,
Turned in bed,
And tossed her arms
Above her head.

The old *Hound* stretched.
And, breathing deep,
He settled down
Again to sleep.

Three O'clock·

The *Rooms* were cold, the *Hearth* was grey:
Asleep in the ashes the *Kobold** lay.
The *Board-Floor* creaked,
The *Grey-Mouse* squeaked,
And the *Kobold* dreamed its ear he tweaked.

* A mischievious spirit or gnome often mentioned in German folktales.

ΚΩΡ;
◖Υ;des.

He wrinkled up
His *Forehead* and *Nose*,
And smiled in his sleep,
And curled his *Toes*.

Four O'clock·

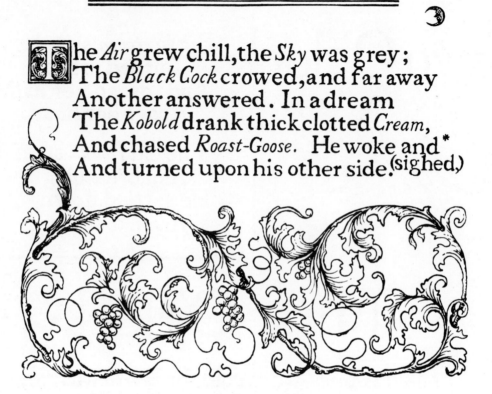

The *Air* grew chill, the *Sky* was grey;
The *Black Cock* crowed, and far away
Another answered. In a dream
The *Kobold* drank thick clotted *Cream*,
And chased *Roast-Goose*. He woke and *
And turned upon his other side. (sighed,)

Five O'clock·

The sleepy *Maid* comes stumbling down
The *Stairs*, while buttoning her *Gown*,
And pokes the fire with a frown.

Up in a rage the *Kobold* flies.
And blows the *Ashes* in her eyes;
"*Plague on the Fire!*" poor *Gretchen* cries.

Sol.
below   *   *   *   *   *   *

The *Goodman* turned about in *Bed,*
And from the *Pillow* raised his *Head*
"*Wife, Wife, its five o'clock!*" he said.

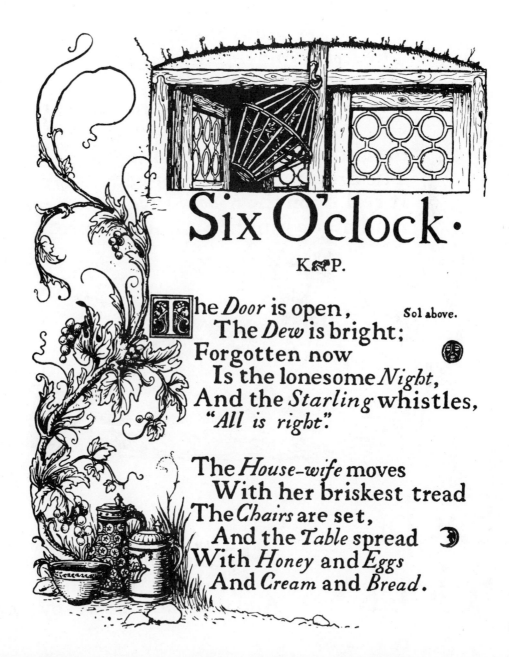

Six O'clock.

K&P.

The *Door* is open,
   The *Dew* is bright;
Forgotten now
   Is the lonesome *Night,*
And the *Starling* whistles,
  "*All is right*".

Sol above.

The *House-wife* moves
   With her briskest tread
The *Chairs* are set,
   And the *Table* spread
With *Honey* and *Eggs*
   And *Cream* and *Bread.*

Seven O'clock·

Around about, ⊙☌⊕E3°26'.
Around about,
The *Kobold* played and in and out;
He peeped in every *Pot* and *Pail*,
And grinned, and pulled the *Pussy's* tail.

Clear.
pleasant.

Big clumsy *Gretchen*, washing up
The *Breakfast-dishes*, dropped a *Cup*;
It fell upon the *Kobold's Toe*,
And made him hop it hurt him so.

Eight O'clock·

The *Sun* in the *Sky*   Grows
Is not yet high,   warmer
And the *Grasses* are wet by the *Pool*.

With hop and jump,
By *Hedge* and *Stump*,
The *Children* are going to *School*.

Nine O'clock·

The *School-bell* rings;
The *Children* all
Must answer to *Cloudy*
The *Master's* call.

and

The *Master* has *warm.*
A crooked *Nose*;
He whips the *Boys*,
And puffs, and blows;

He makes them stand
And walk by *Rule*,
And bow before
They leave the *School*.

Ten O'clock.

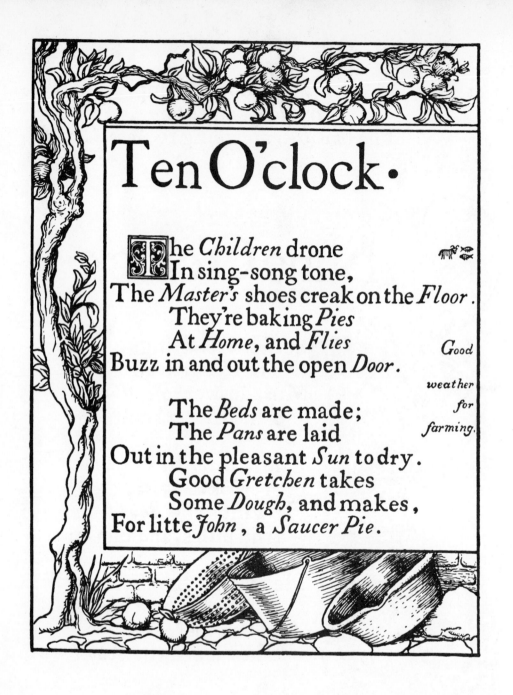

The *Children* drone
In sing-song tone,
The *Master's* shoes creak on the *Floor*.
They're baking *Pies*
At *Home*, and *Flies*
Buzz in and out the open *Door*.

Good

weather

for

farming.

The *Beds* are made;
The *Pans* are laid
Out in the pleasant *Sun* to dry.
Good *Gretchen* takes
Some *Dough*, and makes,
For litte *John*, a *Saucer Pie*.

*Hot
and
dusty.*

The *Cook* undoes the *Oven Door*;
The *Kobold* smells the baking *Pies*;
Licking his *Lips*, with glistening *Eyes*,
He hops across the *Floor*.

Eleven

O'clock·

Our fat, old *Betty* sweats and blows;
   She does not see how near he stands,
   And when she bangs the *Door, Good* *
It'most cuts off his *Nose.*   *Lands!*

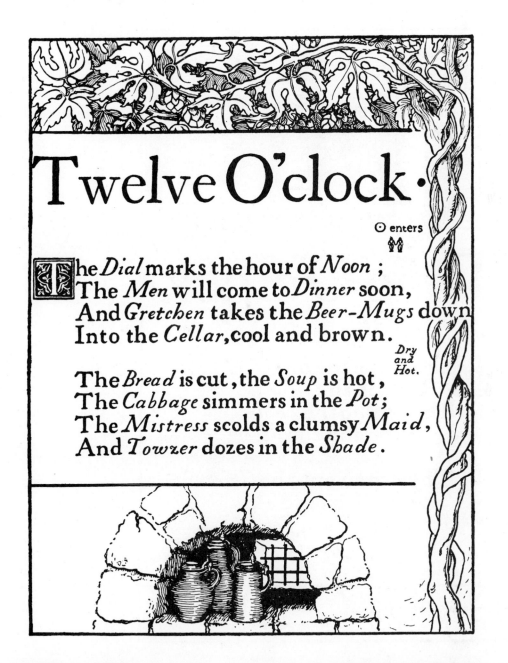

Twelve O'clock·

⊙ enters
♊

The *Dial* marks the hour of *Noon*;
The *Men* will come to *Dinner* soon,
   And *Gretchen* takes the *Beer-Mugs* down
   Into the *Cellar*, cool and brown.

*Dry
and
Hot.*

The *Bread* is cut, the *Soup* is hot,
The *Cabbage* simmers in the *Pot*;
   The *Mistress* scolds a clumsy *Maid*,
   And *Towzer* dozes in the *Shade*.

311

One

The *Kobold* lies,
And blinks his *Eyes*,
Under the *Grape-vine* leaves.
The *Chickens* scratch
In a sunny *Patch*,
And the *Sparrows* fight on the
Eaves.

Hazy.
Very
pleasant.

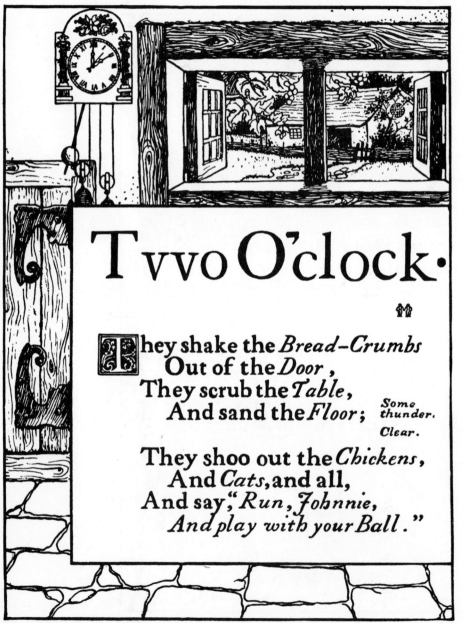

Tvvo O'clock·

They shake the *Bread-Crumbs*
Out of the *Door*,
They scrub the *Table*,
And sand the *Floor*;

Some
thunder.

Clear.

They shoo out the *Chickens*,
And *Cats*, and all,
And say, "*Run, Johnnie,
And play with your Ball*."

The *Bee-Hive* hums;
The *House-wife* comes,
And looks outside the *Door*.
The speckled *Chick*
Hops in, to pick
The *Crumbs* from off the *Floor*.

O'clock.

des.

Three O'clock.

Make
hay.

The *Peddler-Man* is at
the *Door*;
It's *Weeks* since he was
here before.
He gives our little *John*
a *Toy*,
And says he is a fine,
big *Boy*.
The *Mistress* buys some
Flower Seeds,
And *Gretchen* gets some
Pins and *Beads*.

Four O'clock ·

⊙ K.P.U
Warm
and
Dusty .

Bare-necked *Gretchen* combs her hair
At the *Looking-Glass* .
This is *Grease*, and these are *Beads*
She takes to early *Mass* .

Her *Water-Pitcher*, blue and white,
Has got a broken *Nose* ,
And both the *Stockings* that she wears
Are ravelled at the *Toes* .

Five O'clock ·

Pussy-Cat, *Pussy-Cat* what do you dream,
Sleeping out there in the *Sun* ?
The *Red Cow* and *White Cow* are out
in the *Lane* ;
('s pl.
Const. I guess that the *Milking* is done . ⊙
⊕

Pussy-Cat, Pussy-Cat open your *Eyes*,
And see what your *Kitten*'s about ;
She's found a great *Rat-Hole* that's close
to the *Step* ,
And is watching for him to come out.

314

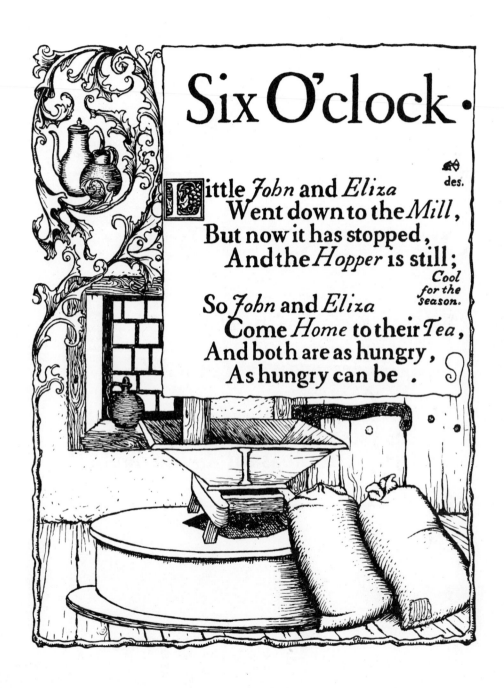

Six O'clock ·

des.

Little *John* and *Eliza*
    Went down to the *Mill*,
But now it has stopped,
    And the *Hopper* is still;
Cool
for the
season.

So *John* and *Eliza*
    Come *Home* to their *Tea*,
And both are as hungry,
    As hungry can be .

Seven O'clock ·

The *Work* is over for the *Day*;
The *Sky* is pale, and far away
The *Village Children* shout at *Play*.

Now from his *Hole* the *Toad* comes out,
And blinks his *Eyes*, and hops about,
And likes the pleasant *Air*, no doubt.

del.
Grows
cool.

Eight O'clock ·

Nine O'clock.

When all are wrapped in *Slumbers* sweet,
About the *House*, with stealthy *Tread*,
With flowered *Gown*, and night-capped
                              Head,
Dame Margery goes, in *Stocking Feet*.

She stops and listens at the *Doors*;
She sees that every thing is right,
And safe, and quiet for the *Night*,
Then goes to *Bed*, and sleeps, and snores.

The little *Bats* fly
About in the *Sky*,
And the *Kobold*'s wide awake.
The great black *Trees*
Are stirred in the *Breeze*,
And a curious *Sound* they make.

Cooler winds.

The *Plays* are done,
And the *Prayers* are said,
And the *Children* are snugly
Tucked in *Bed*.

Ten O'clock.

Out of the *Cupboard*
　　The *Kobold* takes
Some bits of the *Morning*
　　Griddle-Cakes .

*Cold
and
windy.* The *Windows* rattle,
　　The *North Wind* blows,
But the *Ashes* are warm
　　Between his *Toes* .

The little grey *Mouse*
　　Looks out of the *Wall*,
And wishes he had
　　The *Crumbs* that fall.

Eleven O'clock.

Who goes about the *House* when all
　　Are sleeping but the *Clock*,
And no one hears it, all alone,
　　Still saying tick-a-tock?

It is not *Gretchen* goes about,
　　She's snoring in her *Bed*;
It's not the *Hound* that goes about
　　He never lifts his *Head*;

It is the *Wind* that goes about,
　　And sighs around the *House*,
And never wakes the toothless *Hound*,
　　Or stops the gnawing *Mouse*.

Hist! *Hark!*
The *Watch-dogs* bark.
The *Fire* is covered,
　　The *Bricks* grow cold;
In the warmest *Corner's*
　　The brown *Kobold*.

Twelve O'clock.

He sits quite still,
　　And his *Eyes* are bright.
The *Clock* strikes twelve;
　　'Tis the dead of *Night*.

Snuggle down closer
　　Into your *Bed*,
And pull the *Coverlets*
　　Over your *Head*.

Look out for frost.

319

THE  THREE TREES

A dramatic monologue by Tom McNaughton
Visualized by Ray Barber

My scene is a woodland glade.

In the center is a beautiful bubbling spring

surrounded by three trees,

there, there, and there.

Up climbs in the early morn a pretty little rabbit.

It runs through the woodland glade

to quench its pretty little thirst

in the beautiful bubbling spring,

surrounded by the three trees,

there, there, and there.

One morning while the pretty little rabbit

was busily engaged suckling up the nectar

from the beautiful bubbling spring,

surrounded by the three trees,

there, there, and there,

a hunter roaming through the woodland glade

espies the pretty little rabbit.

But, the pretty little rabbit,

having his mouth filled with water,

did not hear the approach of the hunter,

and therefore went on drinking from

the beautiful bubbling spring,

surrounded by the three trees,

there, there, and there.

The hunter raised his gun and fired,

frightening the pretty little rabbit

away from the beautiful bubbling spring,

but leaving the three trees,

there, there, and there.

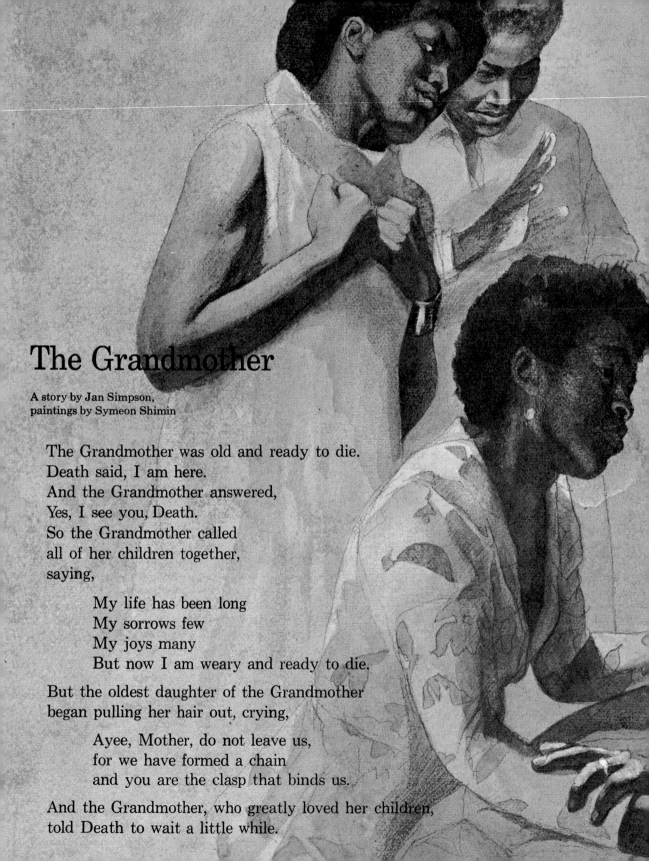

The Grandmother

A story by Jan Simpson,
paintings by Symeon Shimin

The Grandmother was old and ready to die.
Death said, I am here.
And the Grandmother answered,
Yes, I see you, Death.
So the Grandmother called
all of her children together,
saying,

> My life has been long
> My sorrows few
> My joys many
> But now I am weary and ready to die.

But the oldest daughter of the Grandmother
began pulling her hair out, crying,

> Ayee, Mother, do not leave us,
> for we have formed a chain
> and you are the clasp that binds us.

And the Grandmother, who greatly loved her children,
told Death to wait a little while.

The Grandmother lived on and on.
Then again Death said, I am here,
and the Grandmother answered, Yes, I see you, Death.
So the Grandmother called all of her children together, saying

> My life has been long
> My sorrows few
> My joys many
> But now I am weary and ready to die.

But the second daughter of the Grandmother
began beating her breast, crying,

> Ayee, Mother, do not leave us,
> for we have formed a bridge
> and you are the strength that binds us.

And the
      Grandmother,
           who greatly
  loved her children,
told Death
    once more
        to wait
   a little
     while.

The Grandmother lived on and on.
Then a third time Death said, I am here,
and the Grandmother answered, Yes, I see you, Death.
So the Grandmother called all of her children together, saying

> My life has been long
> My sorrows few
> My joys many
> But now I am weary and ready to die.

But the youngest daughter of the Grandmother
began hitting her head upon the ground, crying

> Ayee, Mother, do not leave us,
> for we have formed a circle
> and you are the life that binds us.

And the Grandmother, who greatly loved her children,
even again told Death to wait.

The Grandmother lived on and on.
Then one night as always
the oldest daughter
brought a bowl of cooked meal,
and the second daughter
brought a taste of honey
and the youngest daughter
brought a cupful of cool milk.
The Grandmother ate,
and when she had finished
she called her daughters to her
and kissed them on the lips
and closed her eyes to press the images of them
in her mind.

> Ah, she thought, it is done.
> My children are good and strong.
> My grandchildren are sweet and healthy.
> I have bid them all farewell.
> I have pressed their images in my mind forever.
> And I leave behind my love to light the way.
> I am ready.

And Death came and took her to rest in the kingdom that is his.

Small bird,
forgive me
but I must wait
to hear
the rest of your song
in some other world.

ANONYMOUS

DESIGNED BY DANIELLE MARTIN

Fly away
fly away over the sea
sun-loving swallow
for summer is done;
come again
come again
come back to me
bringing the summer
and bringing the sun.

A POEM BY CHRISTINA G. ROSSETTI

The Hen and the Carp

A POEM BY IAN SERRAILLIER

Once, in a roostery
There lived a speckled hen, and when-
Ever she laid an egg this hen
Ecstatically cried:
"O progeny miraculous, particular spectaculous,
What a wonderful hen am I!"

Down in a pond nearby
Perchance a fat and broody carp
Was basking, but her ears were sharp —
She heard Dame Cackle cry:
"O progeny miraculous, particular spectaculous,
What a wonderful hen am I!"

"Ah, Cackle," bubbled she,
"For your single egg, O silly one,
I lay at least a million;
Suppose for each I cried:
'Oh progeny miraculous, particular spectaculous!'
What a hullabaloo there'd be!"

The Pheasant

A POEM BY ROBERT P. TRISTRAM COFFIN
WATER COLOR BY WILLI BAUM

A pheasant cock sprang into view,
A living jewel, up he flew.

His wings laid hold on empty space,
Scorn bulged his eyeballs out with grace.

He was a hymn from tail to beak
With not a tender note or meek.

Then the gun let out its thunder,
The bird descended struck with wonder.

He ran a little, then, amazed,
Settled with his head upraised.

The fierceness flowed out of his eyes
And left them meek and large and wise.

Gentleness relaxed his head,
He lay in jeweled feathers, dead.

There were three crows sat on a tree.
            Oh, Billy McGee McGaw.
There were three crows sat on a tree.
            Oh, Billy McGee McGaw.
There were three crows sat on a tree.
And they were black as they could be,
And they all flapped their wings and cried,
      "Caw, caw, caw."
            Oh, Billy McGee McGaw.
And they all flapped their wings and cried,
      "Caw, caw, caw."
            Oh, Billy McGee McGaw.

Billy McGee McGaw   AN OLD SONG TO BE SUNG TO THE TUNE OF "WHEN JOHNNY COMES MARCHING HOME"

2 Said one old crow unto his mate,
　　　　Oh, Billy McGee McGaw.
Said one old crow unto his mate,
　　　　Oh, Billy McGee McGaw.
Said one old crow unto his mate,
"What shall we do for grub to ate?"
And they all flapped their wings and cried,
　"Caw, caw, caw."
　　　　Oh, Billy McGee McGaw.
And they all flapped their wings and cried,
　"Caw, caw, caw."
　　　　Oh, Billy McGee McGaw.

"There lies a horse on yonder plain,"
　　　Oh, Billy McGee McGaw.
"There lies a horse on yonder plain,"
　　　Oh, Billy McGee McGaw.
"There lies a horse on yonder plain,
Who's by some cruel butcher slain."
And they all flapped their wings and cried,
　　　"Caw, caw, caw."
　　　Oh, Billy McGee McGaw.
And they all flapped their wings and cried,
　　　"Caw, caw, caw."
　　　Oh, Billy McGee McGaw.

4 "We'll perch ourselves on his backbone,"
       Oh, Billy McGee McGaw.
"We'll perch ourselves on his backbone,"
       Oh, Billy McGee McGaw.
"We'll perch ourselves on his backbone,
And eat his eyeballs one by one."
And they all flapp'd their wings and cried,
    "Caw, caw, caw."
       Oh, Billy McGee McGaw.
And they all flapp'd their wings and cried,
    "Caw, caw, caw."
       Oh, Billy McGee McGaw.

The Ax A story by John R. Dunn, art by Charles Brey

What are you making, Gramps?

I am making an ax, Mimi.
I had rare luck this morning.
I discovered this old steel pick buried beneath the coal.
I will make it into an ax.
It will be better than my stone ax.

What is a pick, Gramps? What is steel?

A pick is a tool.
The ancients used it for digging coal out of the ground.
They made steel from iron ore found in the earth.
From the steel, they made picks and many other wonderful tools.

Were you ever above ground, Gramps?

Yes, Mimi.
I was born above ground, oh so long ago,
but we came here to live when I was very young.

What is it like above ground?
Can we go there some day?

I remember very little about life above ground.
We moved here when I was very very young.
But my parents told me it was wonderful—
green and warm.
I still have a book from above the ground.
I've kept it hidden for you
and you must never tell anyone.
Because it is so damp down here,
I only open the book on important occasions.

What is a book, Gramps?

A book is a record of life.
It is a tool for power.
If you behave down here,
maybe I will show you the book someday.
Then if you are quick and wise,
you can learn to read.
You can learn many of the wonders of the ancients
by reading their books.

But you can never go above ground.
To do so is to die.

Why would I die, Gramps?

You would die,
because the ancients made great tools of war
and fought each other
until all the earth above ground was poisoned.
Most of the ancients died,
but a few of us,
knowing that coal is the sun's storehouse of energy,
moved into these old mines
and learned how to live on coal.
See now how strong and keen this blade of steel becomes.

What will you do with the ax, Gramps?

Why, with the ax, Mimi,
I plan to drive the family of George from the gallery.
Then we will live where the tunnel is dry
and we will own the books.

Usetsu-zu (Snow landscape) Painted by Go-Shun

On moor and mountain
Nothing stirs
This morning of snow.

—Chiyo-ni

He Ain't Heavy...He's My Brother

WORDS BY BOB RUSSELL

The road is long, with many a winding turn,
that leads us to who knows where, who knows where.
But I'm strong, strong enough to carry him;
He ain't heavy, he's my brother.
So on we go; his welfare is my concern.
No burden is he to bear, we'll get there.
For I know he would not encumber me;
He ain't heavy, he's my brother.
If I'm laden at all, I'm laden with sadness
that everyone's heart isn't filled with the gladness
of love for one another.
It's a long, long road,
from which there is no return.
While we're on our way to there, why not share?
And the load doesn't weigh me down at all;
He ain't heavy, he's my brother.

Ace Tory

BY A. MINNY MOOSE

Wants pawn term, dare worsted ladle gull
hoe lift wetter murder inner ladle cordage
honor itch offer lodge, dock florist.
Disk ladle gull orphan worry ladle cluck
wetter putty ladle rat hut,
end, fur disk raisin pimple colder
Ladle Rat Rotten Hut.

Wan moaning Rat Rotten Hut's murder
colder inset:
"Ladle Rat Rotten Hut,
heresy ladle basking winsome burden barter
end shirker cockles.
Tick disk ladle basking
tudor cordage offer grain murder
how lifts honor udder site
offer florist.
Shaker lake!
Dun stopper laundry wrote!
Dun stopper peck floors! Dun daily-daily inner florist,
an yonder nor sorghum stenches
dun stopper torque wet strainers."

"Hoe-cake, murder,"
  resplendent Ladle Rat Rotten Hut,
  end tickle ladle basking an stuttered oft.
  Honor wrote tudor cordage offer grain murder,
  Ladle Rat Rotten Hut mitten anomalous woof.

"Wail, wail, wail," set disk wicket woof,
"evanescent Ladle Rat Rotten Hut!
  Wares or putty gull goring
  wizard ladle backing?"

"Armor goring tumor grain murder's,"
  reprisal ladle gull.
"Grammar's seeking bet.
  Armor ticking arson burden barter
  end shirker cockles."

"O hoe! Heifer blessing woke,"
  setter wicket woof.
  Butter taught tomb shelf.
"Oil tickle shirt court
  tudor cordage offer grain murder.
  Oil ketchup wetter letter.
  End den — oh bore!"

Soda wicket woof tucker shirt court,
end whinny ratched a cordage
offer grain murder,
picket inner winnow
an sore debtor por oil worming worse
lion inner bet.
Inner flesh
disk abdominal woof lipped honor
betting adder rope.
Zany pool down
a grain murder's nut cup end gnat gun,
any curdle dope inner bet.

Inner ladle wile,
Ladle Rat Rotten Hut a raft adder cordage
an ranker dough ball.

"Comb ink, sweat hard,"
setter wicket woof, disgracing is verse.

"Oh, grammer," crater ladle gull.
"Wart bag icer gut!"

"Buttered luck chew whiff, doling,"
whiskered disk ratchet woof,
wetter wicket small.

"Oh, grammar, water bag noise!
A nervous sore suture anomalous prognosis!"

"Buttered small your whiff,"
inserter woof, ants mouse worse waddling.

"Oh, grammar, water bag mousey gut!
A nervous sore suture bag mouse!"

Daze worry on forger nut gull's lest warts.
Oil offer sodden, throne offer carvers
an sprinkling otter bed,
disk curl an bloat Thursday woof
ceased pore Ladle Rat Rotten Hut
an garbled erupt.

MURAL:

Yonder   nor   sorghum   stenches

ladle gulls shut

stopper torque

wet strainers.

When Christmas Comes

A STORY BY DORIS WHITMAN,
PICTURES BY DAVID K. STONE

For three days it snowed without stopping.
The Mallorys couldn't remember
when it had snowed so much.
All the schools were closed.
Snow plows had broken down
because the snow was so heavy.
It was a real snowstorm.

Sara and Tim Mallory talked excitedly
as the flakes drifted down.
But their brother Jake didn't seem to care.
He didn't look up when Tim ran into his bedroom.

"Did you hear the news?" Tim asked,
  his brown eyes shining.
"We're not going to buy a Christmas tree this year.
  We're going to cut our own!
  One of those," he said,
  pointing to the two spruce trees outside Jake's window.
"How do you like that?"

  Jake shrugged. "It's all right," he said.

"You can watch from the window," said Tim,
  trying to get his brother interested.
"I'll yell 'Timm-berr,'
  so you'll know when it's coming down."

Jake said nothing, and went on reading.

Jake felt so left out of it all!
He felt none of the excitement
of their having their own tree.
He couldn't help cut it,
and he hated the idea of sitting at the window
watching the others have the fun.
He decided he wouldn't watch them cut it down,
and he wouldn't help decorate it either.
He didn't want to have anything to do
with their Christmas tree!

Jake had been very ill when he was six years old.
Now he was twelve.
He still wore braces on his legs
and he had to sit in a wheel chair.
He would never be able to run and play
as other children did,
but the doctors said he might walk again
if he really tried.
At first Jake seemed to accept this
and learned to take a few steps on his own.

But as Sara and Tim got older
and Jake heard them tell of all the adventure they had,
he began to lose interest in walking.
He seemed to feel that if he couldn't do
all the things the others did,
there was no point in walking at all.

Mr. Mallory, Tim and Sara
went out to cut the tree on Sunday.
Wrapped in scarves and mufflers,
carrying peanut butter sandwiches
to fortify themselves,
they tramped out into the snow.

With much laughing and pulling and pushing
they brought it at last,
full of snow, onto the porch.
"Now you can start on the decorations,"
said Mr. Mallory.
"Tomorrow we'll bring the tree inside."

Later that afternoon,
Sara took the colored paper
and scissors in to Jake.
"No thanks," said Jake, as she entered the room.
"I don't want to make decorations this year."

"Why not?" asked Sara, disappointed.
"You always make such good ones."

But Jake just shook his head and turned away.
Sara was about to go out,
when suddenly Jake said, "Look!"

He was pointing to the one spruce tree
still standing outside his window.
"Chickadees!"

Sara ran over to see.
The tree was full of little birds.
They were hopping in and out of the branches,
chirping away, as merry as could be.

"They look so happy," said Jake.
"Look how they're jumping around!"

"Those two are fighting over something," said Sara.
"Look, Jake! It's Tim's peanut butter sandwich!
He must have dropped it when we were cutting down the tree."

They spent the rest of the afternoon
watching the little birds.
They stood at the window
until it was too dark to see any more.

The next morning the snow stopped,
and everything was lovely.
The sky was clear and blue,
and everything else was white.
In some places only the very tops
of the bushes could be seen.
The sunlight glistened on the icicles.
It was a wonderful sea of sparkling snow outside.

After breakfast Sara ran to the window to see
if the chickadees were playing in the spruce tree.
But the tree was empty, and there,
lying in the snow were four little birds.

Sara ran as fast as she could to Jake's room,
holding back her tears.
"Jake! Jake! Four of those little chickadees are dead!
Someone killed them!"

Jake quickly wheeled his chair to the window
and looked out at the four dark spots on the snow.

His face turned pale.
"No one killed them," he said quietly.
"They were hungry. That's why they died."

"But we saw them yesterday, eating Tim's sandwich," said Sara.

"That's just it," said Jake.
"That's why there were so many of them yesterday.
They all wanted some of the sandwich.
But there wasn't enough to go around."

Sara burst into tears.
"Oh, Jake," she said,
"I thought those little birds were happy,
and all that time they were starving!"

"We should have put some crumbs out for them,"
Jake said, half to himself.
Suddenly he swung his chair around to face Sara.
"Don't just stand there!" he shouted.
"Go and put some food out for them!
We don't want any more dying around here!"

Sara rushed off to the kitchen,
without another word.
She pulled on her snow pants and jacket,
and waded out into the snow.

As she came close to the spot
where the little birds were lying,
she thought she saw one of them move.
She picked it up carefully
and held it in her hands.
She was sure she could feel it breathing.
Scattering the breadcrumbs on top of the snow,
she hurried back to Jake.

"This one's alive!" she said breathlessly,
carefully holding the little bird to Jake.
Jake held it in his hand and his eyes widened with excitement.
The little heart was beating!

"Sara!" he said. "You're right! It *is* alive!"
He put the bird inside his bathrobe,
holding it against his chest.
"We've got to warm it,
and we've got to get some food into it, too."

"I'll get some breadcrumbs," said Sara.

"No, wait a minute!" said Jake.
"It won't eat breadcrumbs now. Here, I'll try this."
He took some hot cereal from his untouched breakfast tray
and forced the food into the bird's mouth.

Its little head flopped to one side,
and the hot cereal slid down its throat.
Jake fed the bird four or five times.
Sara stood watching, almost afraid to breathe.

Jake could feel his own heart beating
as he put the bird back inside his bathrobe.
"Please don't let it die," he wished silently.

"Sara, see if you can find a small box," he said aloud.
"And get some seeds and water."

"Do you think it will live?" asked Sara in a whisper.

"I think so," said Jake.
"But I need something to put it in. Hurry!"

In a very short time Sara was back,
and she was carrying a shoe box with cotton,
a handful of sunflower seeds,
and a small cup of water in the bottom.
Jake gently placed the chickadee on the soft cotton
and Sara put the box on the radiator.
They leaned over the box,
  watching the little bird closely.
    After a few moments it began to move.

    "Jake! Did you see?"
      whispered Sara excitedly.

                              "It moved."

"I know," said Jake, his eyes shining.
"It's going to get well."

After lunch,
Tim came to join the watch over the little bird.
"Jake really saved it," Sara said proudly.
"He knew just what to feed it,
and what to do with it."

"But what about the other birds?" asked Tim.
"We'd better feed them too, or more will die.
We can put the food in the tree.
That way they'll be able to get at it."

"Oh, let's do that," said Sara, clapping her hands.
"We can tie the food onto the branches."

So they all helped to string apples
and oranges and popcorn balls,
and Tim and Sara went back and forth,
carrying things outside to put in the tree.

At the end of an hour the tree was laden,
and the young Mallorys could be sure
that no more birds would die in their yard.
There were cups of birdseed,
lumps of suet,
peanut butter in tinfoil cups, and mush.
There were pumpkin seeds
and sunflower seeds,
raisins and peanuts,
popcorn balls, apples and oranges
strung from the branches.

"Look, Tim!"
cried Sara, as they finished.
"It's a Christmas tree for the birds!"

Jake was laughing as they walked into his room.
"Take a look at those silly birds," he said.
"They're as good as a circus."

Sara and Tim ran over to his window to look.
The tree was a-flutter with birds.
Chickadees and blue jays
were flying in and out of the branches,
chattering and scolding at each other.
"What's the matter with them?"
asked Tim.

"The blue jays want all the food for themselves," said Jake.
"They're chasing the chickadees away."

"Why don't they all eat together?" asked Sara.

"The sassy things! Go away! Shoo!"
shouted Sara to the blue jays.

"They're hungry, too," said Jake.
"Do you want them to die like the others?
Our little birds will come back after awhile.
Just watch, you'll see!"

A squeak from the box on the radiator
made them all turn around.
They were just in time to see
the little chickadee hop
to the corner of the box
and take a peck at the birdseed.

"It's getting better, all right," said Tim.
"He's going to fly out of here soon.
We'd better get a cage,
if we want to keep him."

"No, you can't do that!" said Jake angrily.
"This is a wild bird!
He's used to being free,
and he'd die if you put him in a cage."

"Gee, Jake," said Sara.
"You really know a *lot* about birds."

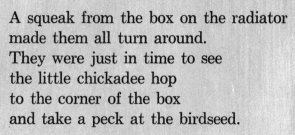

Dinner was very gay that night.
Everyone was happy because Jake had come to the table.
For months he'd been having
his meals in his room, all alone.
He had felt that he couldn't share
in the fun and laughter of the others.
But today things were different.
Jake had things to tell, too.
He was full of excitement from the day's adventures.

So they all laughed together at dinner again,
and Jake talked as much as anyone.

When the meal was over, Mrs. Mallory said,
"Now that the birds have their Christmas tree,
I think it's time for us to begin on ours.
Are you coming to help, Jake?"

"Sure thing!" said Jake.

So it seemed that the holiday season,
which had started out so badly,
was full of hope, after all.

The next afternoon,
Sara and her mother were frosting cookies in the kitchen,
and Tim was putting the wreath up on the door.
Suddenly there was a great shout,
"Tim! Sara! Somebody come here quickly!"

It was Jake.
They all dropped everything and ran to his room.

"There's a hawk after some of the birds!" he cried,
when they came to the door.
"He'll eat the little ones if he catches them.
Please, chase him away!"

But no one moved.
They all stood in the doorway,
staring at Jake.
He was *standing* at the window!

"Please, hurry!" cried Jake.
"They don't even see him yet."

"I'll get him, Jake," said Tim, starting forward.
"I'll get the broom."

They all watched from the window
as Tim dashed out into the snow.
He shouted and shook the broom at the hawk.
After a few minutes it flapped its wings lazily
and flew off.

When the hawk was gone
and Tim was back inside,
Mother said, "Jake, do you know
that you are standing up?
You are standing—alone—all this time!"

"I . . . I didn't even know it!" said Jake,
staring at them.
"I'm standing . . . and I didn't even know.
It must have happened when I saw the hawk."

And then they were all laughing and talking at once.
But Jake didn't say another word.
He just stood very still
and thought, "I'm going to do this every day,
and then, when Christmas comes . . ."

And Christmas was coming quickly now.
There were secrets and whisperings throughout the house,
and every now and then you could hear
the crinkly sounds of wrapping paper.
Every day more presents appeared under the tree.
It was hard not to take a peek,
or feel the packages just a little.

The last few days before Christmas,
Jake's door was closed most of the time.
The others might have thought it strange,
but they were so busy they hardly noticed.
And it was just as well,
because behind his closed door
Jake was busy, too.

At last, it was here!
It was Christmas morning.

"Merry Christmas!" cried Mrs. Mallory,
  as she went into Jake's room to help him to his chair.
"Merry . . ." and she stopped short,
  for there was Jake, sitting in his chair.

"Jake!" cried Mrs. Mallory, in amazement.
"How did you get there?"

"Merry Christmas, Mom,"
  said Jake, smiling.
  And then, before Mrs. Mallory
  could say another word,
  Jake lifted himself from the chair,
  and slowly
  took three steps toward her.
"Mom," he said, "if you'll help me,
  I'm going to walk
  to the Christmas tree."

You should have seen the faces
of the other Mallorys
when Jake walked slowly into the living room,
leaning on Mrs. Mallory's arm.

"Jake!" cried Mr. Mallory, rushing towards him.
"You're walking!" shouted Tim.

"Oh, Jake," said Sara, throwing her arms around him,
and laughing and crying at once.
"You can walk again! How did it ever happen?"

382

Jake hugged her happily.
"Well, almost anything . . . can happen . . .
when Christmas comes!"

Had I the heavens' embroidered cloths,
Enwrought with golden and silver light,
The blue and the dim and the dark cloths
Of night and light and the half-light,
I would spread the cloths under your feet:
But I, being poor, have only my dreams;
I have spread my dreams under your feet;
Tread softly because you tread on my dreams.

A POEM BY W. B. YEATS,
PHOTOGRAPH BY
WILLIAM H. REGAN